A Citizen's Guide to River Conservation

The Conservation Foundation is a nonprofit research and communications organization dedicated to encouraging human conduct to sustain and enrich life on earth. Since its founding in 1948, it has attempted to provide intellectual leadership in the cause of wise management of the earth's resources.

A Citizen's Guide to River Conservation

ROLF DIAMANT
J. GLENN EUGSTER
CHRISTOPHER J. DUERKSEN

 The Conservation Foundation
Washington, D.C.

Cover design by Sally A. Janin, using an illustration by Isabel Mancinelli
Illustrations and maps by Isabel Mancinelli
Typography by Rings-Leighton, Ltd., Washington, D.C.
Printed by R.R. Donnelley & Sons Company, Harrisonburg, Virginia

The Conservation Foundation
1717 Massachusetts Avenue, N.W.
Washington, D.C. 20036

Library of Congress Cataloging in Publication Data
Diamant, Rolf.
    A citizen's guide to river conservation.
    Bibliography: p.
    1. Stream conservation. I. Eugster, J. Glenn. II. Duerksen,
Christopher J., 1948-   . III. Title.
QH75.D52 1984   333.91 '6216   84-7799
ISBN 0-89164-082-7

Contents

Foreword

No more than a handful of cities in the American interior are without a lake or river. Water has been critical to settlement of this country from the time of earliest immigration, for transportation and trade, fisheries and drinking water, and for the fertile, flat bottomlands and valleys ideally suitable for farms and building sites. Rivers have fired our imaginations and enriched our literature as they have defined our sense of place. The sleepy brown Sangamon River, its mud banks and smells, its occasional snake, the mysteries of its undergrowth, its capacity to roll and rise and spread in spring rains are important boyhood associations for me. On many a lazy summer afternoon in my childhood, only the river seemed alive and in motion, always available to play with or just watch. Rivers—big and fabled, like the eight major rivers that drain the contiguous 48 states and define their regions, or small and familiar, like the Sangamon in Illinois— add much to our heritage and quality of life.

Now, however, rivers are under increasing pressure from a number of sources—water projects, pollution, and intense recreational uses, to name just a few. Congress recognized those pressures when it enacted the National Wild and Scenic Rivers Act in 1968, which was designed to protect the best examples of our river heritage. While this legislation helped focus attention on river conservation and afforded protection for a number of important waterways, by and large the law's conservation achievements have been disappointing. Today, less money than ever is being spent on federal and state river conservation programs.

We are hopeful, nevertheless, that people care enough to work to conserve the rivers that are most important to them. Already we are seeing innovative local efforts across the United States to protect such waters and their adjacent settings. These efforts are as diverse as the nation is, and they hold great promise. *A Citizen's Guide to River Conservation* is aimed at helping local citizens, who are the backbone of efforts to conserve local waterways — the ones they know and use for recreation and drinking water, and rely on for economic support. This book provides practical tips and advice for putting together and carrying out a local river conservation plan.

This guide is published as part of The Conservation Foundation's Water Program. This program is focusing on the conservation and better management of America's freshwater supplies, with a particular emphasis on protecting the environmental values that our rivers, lakes, and groundwater aquifers provide.

The rivers of the United States are priceless assets that contribute much to our lives. Growing demands on them will require thoughtful and careful balancing of interests. We hope this book can contribute to that process.

William K. Reilly
President
The Conservation Foundation

Preface

This *Citizen's Guide* is written for all Americans who care about rivers. We believe concerned citizens, working together, can have a positive influence on the future of their local rivers and streams. The guide is intended to help and encourage anyone, regardless of experience, to organize an effective river conservation program where common interests are recognized and a reasonable balance of uses is achieved. It is our hope that you, your friends, and your neighbors will be able to use it to gain a greater voice in determining the future of your river and some control over what life along the river will be like in the years to come.

Rivers and their corridors — the land along the banks — are important to both our economy and our quality of life. River water is used for drinking, irrigation, wildlife habitat, waste treatment, replenishing our groundwater, and many kinds of recreation. River corridors provide some of our finest agricultural soils and contain floodplains that buffer the effects of periodic flooding. River corridors also provide opportunities for transportation and commerce, as well as attractive places to live, work, and relax.

In many areas, the health and attractiveness of a river and river corridor significantly affect the economic well-being of local communities. This is particularly true in areas where communities depend on river resources for drinking water, fishing, or tourism or where a positive perception of the river corridor environment can influence the area's ability to attract new residents and economic investments.

For with all the material benefits our rivers provide us, they also provide for something in our lives that cannot be easily described or measured. Rivers are an escape valve, a link to the past. Nearly all of our American rivers have traditions and associated local folklore that are still passed on from one generation to the next. Rivers also provide for simple pleasures — the enjoyment of living along their banks, guiding a canoe, or fishing from a favorite spot on a bridge.

Throughout this guide, we use the term *river conservation* to mean the wise use of a river and its adjacent shoreline so as to ensure that the value of its many resources, as well as the quality of life for people living near it, will not be diminished over time or forever lost. Conservation is important for all American rivers: the well-known scenic wonders like the Columbia, the Missouri, and the Potomac, as well as the thousands of lesser-known rivers and streams. A river need not be wild or spectacularly scenic to benefit from conservation: often, it is the worst-abused rivers that can benefit the most from diligent efforts to improve their quality.

This guide has been designed to be easy to read and use. Scientific, legal, and planning jargon has been avoided. Some general guidelines have been suggested for achieving citizen involvement and working with people to reach decisions through an open, conciliatory process. In addition, we have described what has been accomplished along several rivers across the United States, perhaps in situations similar to your own. The appendixes provide some useful sources for further information and assistance.

Writing this guide was an idea that would not easily go away for any of us. Rivers are a powerful inspiration, and, though there were frustrating times when we wished we were out enjoying a river instead of writing about one, we kept at it.

I would like to thank my two coauthors: Glenn Eugster, who from the very beginning never doubted our endeavor and gave the guide so much time and careful thought, and Chris Duerksen, the director of this project for The Conservation Foundation, who provided much practical advice and encouragement. I would also like to thank The Conservation Foundation for its interest and support. Particular thanks are due to J. Clarence Davies, the Foundation's executive vice-president, and Edwin H. Clark II, director of the Foundation's Water Program, for their support and encouragement; Bradley Rymph, for his editorial first aid; and Deborah Dorofy for her production assistance. Important sections of the guide were contributed by Jennifer A. Haverkamp, Helene Hollander, Philip C. Metzger, Dan Miller, and Drew Parkin—who deserve much credit for the breadth of material covered. Special thanks are due my friend and colleague Isabel Mancinelli for her excellent illustrations and maps.

A number of people in the field of citizen involvement and river conservation provided ideas and inspiration along the way: Dart Thalman, Dave Gibson, Ralph Goodno, Stephen Andersen, Stan Young, George Macpherson, Ron Mortimore, Greg Moore, and Kathy Kester. I owe a debt to them all.

Last but not least, I would like to thank our tireless reviewers: Katherine Preston, Charlie Morrison, Linc Diamant, and Elizabeth Bell, who weathered our many drafts with good humor and insight. Our most critical reviewer, Nora Mitchell, of the Ipswich Conservation Commission, never lost sight of this guide's audience and purpose—and the importance of finishing it.

Rolf Diamant
Ipswich, Massachusetts

Introduction:
Our Changing Rivers

Throughout the United States, the character of our rivers is rapidly changing. Energy development, dams, urbanization, and a rising demand for water-oriented recreation are all contributing to this change. Too often, however, there has been little direct public involvement in the decisions that guide these changes, even when they affect river qualities that people value most.

What happens upstream on a river can have many effects on individuals and communities downstream. No farm, business, village, or home located near flowing water is immune from an upstream neighbor's water uses and abuses of the waterway. Whether you are an angler or farmer, hunter or homeowner, canoe rental operator or sewage plant technician, your river and its many values cannot be taken for granted.

Persons concerned with river conservation should understand the several forces that have been affecting American rivers for over a century. Only a few rivers across the country have escaped intensive development during that period. Segments of those rivers — found mostly in sparsely populated deserts, forests, and agricultural areas — still have good fisheries and remain free-flowing and unpolluted. However, as competition for energy and water resources has grown, these pristine river stretches have become increasingly attractive locations for water and power projects. In New England, for example, only 5 percent of the total river mileage remains free-flowing, according to a recent federal inventory. Nevertheless, proposals for 30 to 40 new hydroelectric dams — up to 75 percent of recent dam permit applications in that region — have been made for those river segments.*

Pressures of a different nature are occurring on remaining free-flowing rivers in the West. Accelerated agricultural production and a continuous expansion of cultivated acreage is outstripping the groundwater supply. More wells are being sunk, and existing wells are reaching deeper and deeper for water, as key agricultural aquifers from Nebraska to California are being exhausted. Attempts to regulate the use of groundwater or to shift production to less-water-demanding crops have made little headway as, one by one, free-flowing rivers have been siphoned off into aqueducts and water projects to irrigate yet more land.†

In addition to hydropower and water diversions, water pollution (including erosion and acid rain), shoreline development, and river recreation have been significantly affecting American rivers. Urbanization, in particular, has often led to widespread pollution and poorly sited and maintained waterfront development. Fortunately, however, since the implementation of the 1972 amendments to the Federal Water Pollution Control Act (now known as the Clean Water Act), many of the rivers harmed by urbanization have begun to revive. The challenge now facing communities along these rivers is to ensure that the enormous public investment that has been made to clean up this pollution is protected, so that the quality of the waterways does not decline again.

Yet, despite the improvement in this aspect of river quality,

---

* For more information on the role of hydropower in New England and an excellent discussion of potential conflicts with other river uses and possible resolutions, see *Water, Watts, and Wilds*, the final report of the former New England River Basin Commission's Hydropower Expansion Study, August 1981.

† There is a good discussion of the politics, economics, and ecology of irrigation in California's Central Valley in Tim Palmer, *Stanislaus: The Struggle for a River* (Berkeley, Calif.: University of California Press, 1982.)

the numerous other forces affecting American waterways continue to have direct, adverse impacts on many of the river uses that we often take for granted (these issues are discussed in greater detail in chapter 2):

- Dam construction often damages both freshwater and anadromous (migratory) fisheries and causes a loss of wildlife habitat and land uses for humans along a river. It also reduces water quality and lessens white-water recreational opportunities.

- Water diversions, if they are large enough, cause rivers and streams to dry up, particularly in dry seasons or times of drought. Reduced water flow can hurt downstream water users who depend on a river for fishing, irrigation, or water supply.

- "Nonpoint-source" water pollution, contamination entering a body of water from dispersed sources over a large area, sometimes degrades water quality even on rivers with newly built sewage-treatment facilities. Nonpoint pollution can include acid rain, runoff of agricultural chemicals and eroded soils, and storm-water runoff from urbanized or industrial sites. Unlike pollution that can be traced to a specific "point," or site (the type of pollution controlled with some success by the Clean Water Act), this type of pollution is difficult to contain.

- Shoreline development is changing the appearance and use of many rivers, particularly those that are easily accessible from urban areas or were recently rehabilitated through the Clean Water Act. Unless it is carefully planned, such development can deny taxpayers many of the anticipated benefits of pollution-control projects — notably, water open to the public for fishing and swimming.

- The growth of recreation (for example, boating and rafting) on rivers, particularly on those rivers that are still largely undeveloped, often has increased fire hazards, trespassing, litter, and noise in cases where public facilities have been inadequate or where planning, coordination, and control of activities have been deficient.

1. Getting Started: Some Guidelines

One of the greatest conservation challenges in the United States today may be restoring or protecting American rivers. Yet river conservation can be one of the most difficult types of conservation efforts. Rivers often flow across town, county, and state boundaries and through many different types of land. Acting alone, a single organization or level of government seldom can achieve the political agreement necessary to conserve river resources, especially if other groups perceive that their interests are being ignored or threatened.

If you are involved in a river conservation effort, you need to recognize the importance of getting the public's attention at the beginning of your work. To do this well, you must understand not just your river but also the people who live along it. Conservation, particularly in rural areas, must be relevant to people's lives and their plans for the future.

Just as important, you must be cooperative, flexible, and willing to form coalitions of concerned citizens. You should understand the points of view of different river-related interests. When the community relations process is carried out successfully, it creates an atmosphere that allows the consideration of a broad range of conservation actions. When community relations are ignored or handled poorly, however, mistrust, hostility, and confrontation may result, making any solution impossible.

Some basic guidelines for beginning a project can help you in getting your community involved and in setting your priorities. Many of these guidelines are simple principles for organization and public involvement and should be applied where they make the most sense.

Get to Know Your River Environment Well

No two river conservation projects will involve exactly the same set of goals. You should learn everything about the resource values of your river area as soon as you can. Identify the features of your river (for example, special botanical and historic areas) and the traditional land-use patterns (like dairy farming or forestry) that give your river corridor its special character. Examine the extent to which activities such as mining, water diversions, dams, and logging are causing problems along the river. Study whether proposed bridge or utility crossings or nearby road improvements are a problem.

Be sure to familiarize yourself with issues or problems that are on people's minds. Look at river-related issues through the eyes of neighbors and other people who have lived near or along the river for some time. Whenever possible, spend time with people who know the river well and get to know them. Consider surveying area residents, including riverfront landowners and local officials. This can be a useful tool for making initial contact with all concerned individuals and for learning about their feelings toward uses of the river. A well-worded questionnaire can focus the respondents' attention on present or future problems along the river and perhaps get them thinking about the river as an important resource, not to be taken for granted. A survey can be administered by personal interview, phone, or mail to landowners, local officials, and other concerned citizens.

Talk with river resource users, such as farmers, anglers, and boaters, particularly people who make their living on or near the river. If some people are worried that rapid land-use change, resource depletion, or water pollution might cost them their jobs, make the connection between those issues and river conserva-

tion objectives. If, however, there are perceptions that your conservation objectives pose a greater threat to local jobs or quality of life, you may need to address those fears directly and to discuss the potential economic benefits and costs of achieving a healthy and attractive river environment. If your region is largely dependent on tourism, make the connections between environmental quality, the attractiveness of the local river, and the future prosperity of the tourist industry and all who depend on it. You might also remind public officials that sport anglers, who probably would be more apt to use an unpolluted river, contribute millions of dollars each year to the economics of river communities throughout the United States. Another economic benefit worth mentioning is the possible revitalization of downtown waterfront businesses. (See appendix G.)

Contact Key Community Leaders Early

It is important that a good first impression be made on public officials. Show a positive attitude from the start. Flexibility, patience, and an attitude of dealing with equals create a climate favorable to cooperation. Know who important decision makers are and the ways in which they can affect the river's future. You may need to get better acquainted with state and county legislatures, several town councils, zoning boards, and river-based businesses. Individuals and private organizations that are influential in the affairs of your community and who are interested in the future of the river should also be contacted and involved as early as possible. The broader your spectrum of support, the more likely that your goals will be realized. The "ripple" effect of a good network can save you considerable energy and ensure that you miss no important bases.

Be sure to contact all appropriate elected public officials before you initiate river conservation activities. This, at least, is a basic courtesy. Local officials can be an invaluable source of assistance and information. Bear in mind that home rule is a powerful principle in almost all communities, especially towns and small villages. But, since river conservation activities often must cut across jurisdictional lines and involve other governments, they are sometimes perceived as a threat to home rule. It is, therefore, important that you treat town governments with respect and consult them frequently, even if they at first do not appear to support your efforts. Most river conservation projects will require local involvement and commitment.

Try to get landowners involved in the conservation process, too. Find out what they like and don't like about the river, and encourage in them a sense of stewardship for the river qualities they value most. Attempt to reach a consensus with them on river conservation objectives before you get into detailed discussion of implementation techniques. Often, misconceptions and confusion about such conservation techniques as acquisition, easements, or setbacks can alarm landowners and prevent discussion.

Businesses and industries located near rivers also can be important, influential allies in conservation work. Companies are almost always sensitive about their corporate image among their neighbors and customers. Businesses should be encouraged to endorse and support river conservation efforts as a valuable opportunity to demonstrate their community interest and civic responsibility. If your river valley is an attractive place to live and raise families, area corporations who recruit from outside may directly benefit from river conservation by promoting the area's attractiveness to prospective employees. Many businesses, such as restaurants and stores, also can benefit from increased recreational use and passive enjoyment of the river.

Finally, water-resource developers also have an interest in river conservation since they seek to avoid unnecessary confrontation and project delay in planning new facilities and expanding existing ones. Work with these developers whenever possible to formulate a balanced approach to resource conservation and use. It is in everyone's interest — including your own — to identify appropriate river segments for water-resource development if such development is necessary. Contact companies or agencies that might be looking at your river as a candidate for a project early in their planning before they begin to commit substantial time and capital toward the project. If planners know that significant public opposition and expensive delays are possible, they might choose a different location or project alternative.

Be Accessible to All Interested Parties

Let people know who you are, how you can be reached, and how they can become involved. Try to get to know your opponents as people first and to break down any obvious mutual misconceptions. No community or group wants to feel that a decision has been imposed on it, and most people will react adversely to a decision that they perceive has been made without their having a say. This does not mean that everyone will be satisfied with the outcome of every decision, but people should feel at least that their views have been heard and given consideration. The process should be accepted as fair by people who either would like to participate or would be most affected by the decision. As a result, your river community should begin to feel a greater sense of partnership and responsibility for the river.

Develop Methods for Distributing Information

Stay in close touch with the local media. Get to know media people and how they do their job. Learn what kinds of information are most appropriate for them, with the most potential interest for their readers, listeners, or viewers.

Communicate any announcement or information to the media and all potentially interested parties at the same time. Nobody likes to learn something secondhand or later than everyone else. Particularly in small communities, news or information travels fast.

Focus on an Issue of Community Concern

If a readily perceived threat to your community exists, base your organization around it. Even though your initial efforts may have a narrow focus and may not address any long-term strategies for river conservation, this approach is an effective way to build support and greater awareness in your area and to lay the groundwork for future progress.

Get on Other People's Agendas

See if you can get some time to present your ideas at other groups' regular meetings. When you do, you probably won't have much time, so be well prepared and relevant. In particular, link with other related efforts. Often, groups who might be in competition for use of river resources, such as canoeists and anglers, can resolve their problems by working together on a common issue. Be flexible in your attempts, however. Don't expect that many people will want to attend a meeting about the river, to read your literature, or to agree with your priorities.

Keep Your Objectives Simple and Understandable

Beware of jargon in anything you say or write. If you cannot express your ideas in plain English, they probably need rethinking. If you use illustrations in anything you publish, keep them simple and easily understood. Be careful not to assume that the people you work with or talk to necessarily have much knowledge of your subject. Many people are likely to be unfamiliar with conservation techniques and terminology. Do not provide an unwanted torrent of information, or many people may not bother with it. Make sure that you can explain whatever activity you are doing or proposing; be willing to do so again and again if necessary.

Learn from Other River Conservation Efforts

No matter how unusual you judge your own circumstances, you may be surprised how many rivers and river groups face similar problems. Special skills in such areas as organizing, fund-raising, lobbying, and media work, as well as technical information on shoreline zoning or land trusts, can be shared.*

Prepare a Detailed River Conservation Plan †

Developing a river conservation plan is not a requirement for effective river conservation work, but it can be very helpful in setting the priorities for your effort. Such a plan not only details strategies for getting a river conservation project implemented but also spells out procedures for the management of the program once you have succeeded in getting it established. This plan can be particularly valuable in helping you form a partnership between public and private interests.

---

* See the appendixes and bibliography for lists of conservation contacts and further sources of information. The American River Conservation Council in Washington, D.C., is a particularly valuable clearinghouse for this kind of experience and information.

† Much of the river conservation planning process outlined in this section is adapted from a National Park Service publication, *Greenway Planning: A Conservation Strategy for Significant Landscapes* (1983). That guide was developed to aid in the conservation of large "cultural landscapes," where people live and work, such as the New Jersey Pinelands, the Columbia River Gorge of Washington and Oregon, and the Thousand Islands area of New York and Canada.

Timing and public interest are critically important in developing a river conservation plan. You should begin working on such a plan only when you are certain the circumstances are right and the potential benefits of a plan to your project seem clear. Tailor your plan to the characteristics of your particular river and to the people who own, use, and govern the area.

1. *Develop a preplanning strategy.* Set up a series of discussions with key public and private community leaders to explain the purposes behind establishing a plan and the approaches that could be used to prepare it. These meetings should also help identify funding sources and the people who will do much of the work on the project. (These meetings could be held as part of the process of making key contacts described earlier in this chapter.)

2. *Set up an advisory committee.* Establishing a committee of landowners, representatives of community organizations, and appropriate government officials to guide you in the development of your plan can help maintain citizen involvement throughout the project. Committee members should, of course, be knowledgeable about your river, concerned about its conservation and able to work easily with people.

3. *Establish some goals for your effort.* Although you should already have your own opinions of the important issues affecting your region, it is important that you work with all the communities and major interests along your river to assess each issue, so you can cooperatively determine not only what problems exist but also their causes, effects, and magnitude, the key interests involved, and the questions that need to be answered. After these details are understood by everyone involved in your project, you can work together to establish specific goals for the effort.

4. *Assemble detailed information on your river and its most important features.* You should find it helpful to gather together and organize all the information you have collected — including whatever public consensus has been reached on the relative importance of particular river resources — as you begin to consider the options for your program. One step might be to prepare maps showing the location of these resources, if no maps already have been made.

5. *Evaluate conservation programs and techniques*. You can assume that private organizations and landowners, as well as local governments, will have to play a significant stewardship role. Consider making use of a variety of land conservation tools — including easements, voluntary agreements, land purchases, tax incentives, and zoning ordinances — as well as state and local government permitting regulations. (These tools are discussed in chapter 3.) Existing public programs may need to be strengthened, and new ones might be required. You should also examine potential opportunities for working through private nonprofit organizations such as land trusts (see chapter 4).

Wherever possible, look at opportunities for modifying existing institutional arrangements (for example, county or multitown compacts) to deal specifically with your objectives. You may wish to list all your possible options and then concentrate on those actions that appear to be the most practical and potentially effective and to have broad-based public support. Be sure to consider ways to secure funding for implementing your plan.

6. *Formalize your completed plan*. Summarize and combine all the information collected in the previous tasks. Remember to write the plan so that it is easy to understand. Include a map of existing and proposed land uses along the river. Carefully explain each action that you are recommending, detailing the strategies you hope to follow and the responsibilities you foresee for area governments, private organizations, businesses, and individuals. Identify your expected sources of funding and specify one private organization or coalition of government units to serve as a focus for carrying out the plan.

2. Understanding the Issues

S everal common forces are profoundly affecting the future of all types of rivers throughout the United States. The growth of hydroelectric dams and water diversions certainly are among the most dramatic influences on rivers. However, more subtle yet far more pervasive influences, such as nonpoint-source water pollution, shoreline development, and even the growth of river recreation, are substantially changing the character and quality of our rivers. If you have a broad sense of the problems facing most American rivers, you may be better able to understand whatever particular problems are confronting your own river and community.*

Dams and Water Projects

Dams and other water projects undertaken for flood control, navigation, water supply, and power generation have always posed special challenges to river conservation. Their impacts are often immediately visible and dramatic in ways that water pollution and other threats are not. One of the first environmental disputes in the United States involved the damming of the Tuolumne River in Yosemite National Park in 1913. Conservationists ultimately lost that battle, but a movement was born. During the 1960s and

---

* Additional sources of information about these issues can be found in the bibliography.

1970s, river-based environmental conflicts intensified, as states continued to seek water projects built by the U.S. Army Corps of Engineers and other federal agencies.

Water projects can adversely affect rivers in a number of ways. Dams are often built on undeveloped river stretches that have steep gradients and are the most scenic and best for white-water boating. A dam can inundate many miles of river, and, when completed, its fluctuating water discharges can repeatedly change water temperatures and oxygen levels.

Sometimes a dam can create a new fishery (as when the cold-water discharge from a high dam provides a new site for trout fishing), but, as often, the consequences for fish of the flooding and the reduced water flow caused by the dam are adverse. The greatest impacts are loss of habitat and hindrance of fish spawning and migration. For example, flooding for a dam can affect upstream nursery and spawning grounds. Dams create physical obstructions for fish like salmon and shad that ascend rivers from the sea to breed, as well as for freshwater species that migrate seasonally. Fishways and ladders can help reduce the damage, but studies show that the number of fish migrating upstream is still reduced by 10 to 20 percent at each obstacle. Moreover, passage facilities are expensive to build and generally do not provide much help to downstream migrating fish, which must follow the flow of water over spillways or through conduits and turbines where injury or death can result.

In recent years, the skyrocketing cost of water projects has slowed Congress's approval of many big developments, but increasing oil prices and national energy legislation have spurred some types of projects, such as small hydropower dams.

In 1978, Congress began enacting legislation that, when coupled with energy shortages, led to an unprecedented increase in proposals to build small hydropower projects on rivers across the United States. The Public Utilities Regulatory Policies Act (PURPA), passed in that year, required utilities to buy hydrogenerated power from anyone wanting to sell it. PURPA was followed in 1980 by the Windfall Profits Tax and then the Energy Security Act, which created lucrative investment tax

credits and other tax benefits for developers of hydro projects.*
As a result, the Federal Energy Regulatory Commission (FERC),
which has regulatory authority over small hydropower projects,
received over 1,800 preliminary permit site applications in
1982—up from just 12 in 1976. This "hydromania" subsided
somewhat in 1983 in the face of declining oil prices, but prac-
tically every major American river that can be canoed is still being studied for small-scale hydropower projects.

Some of the problems caused by dams—notably, water
temperature fluctuations—can be avoided through careful design
and management of a project. Others, such as flooding and
obstruction of fish migration routes, are more problematic. But,
with planning and communication, some conflict can be avoided. For example, the New England River Basin Commission
prepared a regionwide study to provide guidance and direction
for locating potential hydropower sites with minimal environmental and competing-use conflicts. The National Park Service is
working closely with the Bonneville Power Administration, the
Pacific Northwest Power Planning Council, four Pacific Northwest
states, and other interests to plan more orderly energy facility
development to conserve significant free-flowing river sections.

Water Diversion and Minimum Flow

The diversion of large amounts of water from streams and rivers
to satisfy agricultural, municipal, and industrial demands is
becoming a problem across the United States. This water may
never be returned to the waterway, and, if it is, is often degraded
in quality. In the West, where water is scarce and there is a long
history of diversion, many rivers have no flow at all during much
of the year. And the problems of large-scale diversions is even
beginning to affect streams in the moist Southeast.

Most diversions do not occur in the stream headwaters, which
may be a river's most valuable part for recreational purposes. In-

---

* National conservation groups are now working to amend these three laws
  to provide greater protection for river resource values during the project
  review process. Citations for these laws can be found in appendix F.

stead, the water is usually taken out farther downstream nearer the point where it is to be used. In western states, this means that old downstream diversions may guarantee the supply of water in the upstream reaches. However, diversion of water from one river basin into another, new mining, or other developments can cause large depletions in the upstream reaches of a waterway.

Reduced flow in streams, particularly during the dry summer months when the demand for water is highest, can diminish a waterway's scenic qualities and create serious "instream" problems for fish and other aquatic wildlife populations. In addition, keeping sufficient water in the stream to allow boating and other recreational uses can be difficult.

Fortunately, awareness of this problem has been increasing. The U.S. Department of the Interior's Fish and Wildlife Service has developed techniques for determining the minimum flow required to support different instream uses. Many states (particularly in the West) that, in the past, have not considered instream flow as an important concern are changing their laws so as to protect such uses. In many cases, however, these efforts are occuring too late to avoid the diversion of massive amounts of water for other purposes, and enforcement of the laws is often spotty. And even now, with the exception of a few states like Oregon, little attention is being given to maintaining the vegetation beside a waterway's banks, which often provides valuable wildlife habitat. Along many rivers from which large amounts of water have been diverted, the vegetation has simply dried up and the habitat has disappeared.

Water Pollution

The most serious water pollution problems are usually caused by industrial and municipal discharges, leakage from septic tanks, drainage from mining operations, and storm-water runoff from agricultural lands. Construction sites, urbanized areas, and timbering operations can also cause serious problems. In some instances, the problem may stem from polluted groundwater seeping into the river during low-flow periods or even a "natural" source, such as a salt bed or normal geological erosion.

Some pollutants directly threaten human health. Disease-causing bacteria and viruses leak from septic tanks, are discharged by municipal sewage systems, and are carried off pasture, grazing lands, or animal feedlots by storm water. Some are carried by wild animals and, therefore, are present even in remote headwaters far removed from human activities. Noxious chemicals are discharged in large volumes by industries and municipal sewer systems and occur in lower concentrations in pollution from other sources. Intense boiling or other forms of water treatment can usually destroy bacteria and viruses but may have no effect on other harmful substances.

Other pollutants may pose less serious direct health effects but significantly diminish a river's attractiveness and ability to support aquatic wildlife. Sediment turns water muddy and may eliminate desirable species of fish. Organic wastes (for example, dead vegetation, animal and human wastes) use up the oxygen normally dissolved in the water, reducing the river's ability to support many types of aquatic life and, in extreme cases, making it noxious. Nutrients from fertilizers and organic wastes stimulate plant and algae growth, creating green-colored rivers and weed-filled ponds out of once clear water courses and lakes.

The effects of some pollutants may be only temporary. Sediment tends to settle out of the water, particularly in areas where the current slows. Natural bacteria in the water decompose organic wastes, and the dissolved oxygen consumed in the process is gradually replenished by natural forces. The rate at which these natural cleansing processes occur depends on the specific conditions in the river; severe pollution can overtax a river's capacity to assimilate and dilute pollutants.

Many pollutants are unaffected by such processes, however, and are carried downstream unchanged. Some, such as heavy metals and other insoluble substances, may accumulate in the river sediments or in fish and other aquatic wildlife, causing problems long after the original pollution source has been cleaned up. Polychlorinated biphenyls (PCBs) dumped into the Hudson River, for instance, may remain on the bottom for hundreds of years, making fish unsafe to eat. And some pollutants (for example, fertilizers and organic wastes) can become a permanent part of the river's ecosystem, taking part in various chemical and biological cycles that may disrupt the river's natural ecological stability.

The most serious water-quality problems usually occur during the summer when water flow is low, even though most pollutants are likely to enter the river during high flow periods. When water flow is high, the pollutants may be diluted sufficiently to avoid serious water-quality problems. However, if the pollutants are not carried out of the river system, they may contribute to problems later.

With the 1972 amendments to the Clean Water Act, the United States began an intensive effort to eliminate industrial and municipal water pollution. Substantial progress has been made in controlling discharges from industrial sites (although many problems still remain). Control of municipal systems has been less successful. Their pollution problems may remain even after pollution-control equipment has been installed, since the equipment often is not operated properly.

Although much effort has been devoted to reducing pollution from industrial facilities, municipal waste-treatment plants, and other "point" sources (that is, sites from which effluents are discharged), very little has been done to control "nonpoint" sources of pollution. Those sources can be quite varied: erosion from cropland and other agricultural sources that transports nutrients, pesticides, and other contaminants; erosion from forestry operations; acid rain; storm-water and other drainage from mine sites; and storm-water runoff from urbanized areas, industrial facilities, construction sites, and highways. Significant amounts of erosion also occur as mountains and hills are worn down naturally.

Nonpoint-source pollution can be a serious problem anywhere except in the most undeveloped areas. And, even there, natural pollutant buildup can contribute large amounts of sediment, nutrients, and other substances that can degrade water quality.

Cropland and rangeland are major sources of sediment. Cropland, for example, produces almost 2 billion tons of soil erosion each year. Much of this erosion never reaches a stream or river, but that which does can carry with it nutrients, pesticides, bacteria, and organic materials. Depending on the particular characteristics of the soil, area topography, and crop patterns, erosion rates can be as high as 100 tons an acre a year. Over 1 billion tons of erosion occur annually on rangeland, primarily in the West, and this sediment can carry with it the same contaminants as soil from cropland erosion, though normally in lower concentrations. In addition to cropland and rangeland, pastureland and forestland each account for less than half a billion tons of erosion a year, roads less than 200 million tons a year, and construction sites less than 100 million tons a year.*

Heavy sediment loads caused by erosion not only turn clear streams muddy but also increase flooding, destroy fish spawning grounds, and substantially diminish the attractiveness of a river for recreation. If sediment buildup continues for a long period, a river can turn from a clear, steep-banked, deep stream into a shallow, "braided" stream that meanders through heavy silt deposits. The nutrients that accompany the sediment stimulate the growth of algae and weeds in lakes and ponds. The pesticides can kill the aquatic life and make the water unsafe to drink. Other types of nonpoint sources, such as mines, can pollute rivers through drainage of toxic metals and acid wastes.

Although the U.S. Department of Agriculture's Soil Conservation Service has been actively attempting to control soil erosion for the past 50 years, little of its attention has been focused on improving water quality. During the late 1970s, a substantial amount of planning took place on nonpoint-source control, but only in a few states did any active programs continue into the 1980s. However, the Clean Water Act may be amended to require that states take more aggressive action to control nonpoint sources of water pollution.

In addition to problems caused by soil erosion, some nonpoint-source water pollution comes—directly or indirectly—from the

---

* For more information on the problem of cropland erosion, see Sandra S. Batie, *Soil Erosion: Crisis in America's Croplands?* (Washington, D.C.: The Conservation Foundation, 1983).

air. An example is acid rain, which is affecting lakes and rivers throughout the United States but particularly in the Northeast. It results from the chemical transformation of pollutants that may have been emitted into the air hundreds of miles away. While being carried through the atmosphere, these pollutants combine with water vapor to form weak sulfuric and nitric acids, which fall to the earth in rain and snow. Sometimes this acid is neutralized (or "buffered") by alkaline compounds in the soil, but, where it is not, it can build up sufficiently in lakes to destroy all fish life and also is suspected of affecting plants, trees, and aquatic wildlife in other places, including rivers.

New federal legislation probably is required before strong steps can be taken to prevent acid rain. The only actions people in affected areas can take are to monitor the acidity of their lakes and streams and to add lime or some other alkaline compound to those waters when the acidity climbs too high.

Shoreline Development

Another force that affects many rivers — again an often obvious one — is shoreline residential, commercial, and industrial development. The most acute and recurring problems are usually associated with residential growth, particularly second-home developments.

During the 1970s, the great outdoors was subdivided as never before. From Vermont to Hawaii, from Minnesota to Florida, pastures, swamps, and forests were sold for leisure property. As the economy picks up steam again in the 1980s, the trend is expected to continue. These recreational developments not only can quickly degrade the aesthetic value of a river corridor if they are designed poorly but also can lead to water-quality problems because of inadequate sewage treatment or faulty septic tanks. Usually, second-home developments are simply not built to the standards required of first homes.

Of equal concern in the future will be residential growth connected with the continuing movement of people in the United States to small towns and rural areas. Rivers in many of the remoter areas have been protected in many cases simply by their distance from population centers, but those days are coming to an end in many areas of the country. Although large-lot river shoreline developments are becoming increasingly popular with new residents who want the benefits of the countryside, these developments bring with them the land-use challenges of urban areas with which rural jurisdictions are usually not prepared to cope. Although these developments are often better designed than are second-home projects, they still can damage scenic river corridors and river ecosystems unless they are carefully sited.

River Recreation

Most people who use rivers for recreational purposes would not consider themselves to be potential conservation threats, but the United States is witnessing an explosion in river-related recreational demand that has begun to have a serious impact on many rivers. Available leisure time, increased mobility, and popular interest in outdoor recreational pursuits have increased dramatically at the same time that the public has rediscovered many cleaned-up rivers, long neglected because of pollution. Studies suggest that canoeing on many popular rivers is increasing at a rate of

25 to 50 percent annually. Many rivers suitable to commercial white-water rafting have, during the past decade, experienced a nearly 100-fold increase in use. Inner-tube riding is growing in popularity, and rafts and kayaks are now seen on rivers where they were previously unknown. Urban boating—including canoeing, sailing, and motor boating—is also becoming more popular, as is passive enjoyment of river settings. Fishing, once the sole form of recreation on many rivers, continues as a major pastime.

Ironically, the upsurge in river recreational demand has paralleled increased competition for water resources, causing a marked decline in recreational opportunities. Hydropower and riverfront residential development, for example, have had major impacts on river recreation. Throughout the United States, free-flowing river stretches that are accessible to canoes or rafts are becoming fewer and harder to get to each year. Similarly, nonrecreational uses, particularly hydropower development, threaten opportunities for sport anglers, as well as programs to reintroduce anadromous fish like salmon.

As recreational opportunities provided by rivers are lost each year to new dams and development, the recreational pressure on remaining free-flowing segments of waterways is rapidly building. This pressure, if concentrated on a limited area, can cause a variety of physical and social problems. Water-quality degradation, soil erosion, disruption of wildlife, trampling of shoreline vegetation, and increased danger of fire are all associated with heavy recreational use, particularly indiscriminate camping.

In addition, much of the controversy involving increased recreational use of rivers inevitably focuses on social concerns, such as overcrowding, noise, and a decline in the quality of recreation. Some people are drawn to rivers to enjoy beauty and solitude, qualities that are the first to suffer from overcrowding or overuse. Recreationists who have other objectives, perhaps the camaraderie of floating a river with exuberant friends, may have different thresholds or tolerances for increased use of a waterway. Different perceptions and expectations can lead to antagonism between river users, between nonmotorized and motorized boaters, commercial outfitters and small private excursionists.

These pressures and problems are not only felt by river users. They also have a major impact on public and private land managers and landowners along the river. On rivers where people long felt free to do as they wished, changes in recreational demand now require some level of management or regulation.

Recreation management does not necessarily imply restricting access to or use of a river, which is often either very costly or controversial to enforce. Two planning tools that have experienced considerable success are recreation zoning—the separation of different types of activities along the river—and periodic rotation of heavy-use areas such as boat launches and campgrounds. One low-cost management approach that can help foster a sense of stewardship among river users is the encouragement of self-policing, through cooperative agreements with organized users (for example, canoe clubs or commercial outfitters).

Whose responsibility is it to take some action and do something about recreational river use? Along river corridors where there are many public holdings, the responsibility for recreation management may rest with a public agency or authority. However, along river corridors where ownership is primarily private, the responsibility and authority may not be clearly defined. In either case, river recreation remains a potential major conservation issue, often requiring a cooperative planning effort on the part of landowners, river users, commercial interests, and government.

3. Using Basic Conservation Tools

Before you can choose the strategy best suited to your conservation goals, you need to understand a few basic land conservation tools. As growth pressures on rivers increase across the United States, river conservation organizations and governments are responding with a wide variety of approaches, including techniques for achieving voluntary conservation (such as easements, voluntary agreements, land purchases, and tax incentives) and methods for using government regulations (particularly zoning ordinances and project permitting).*

Easements

An easement is the right of a nonowner of a piece of property to use the land for a specific purpose (for example, the right of access or the right to cut timber). Easements have been used by conservationists to protect such waterways as the Upper Delaware River in New York and Pennsylvania and Brandywine Creek in Pennsylvania and Delaware (both of these projects are described in chapter 4).

---

* A number of useful references on land conservation tools, as they apply in various states, are listed in the bibliography. For a more generic discussion of tools, see *The Use and Protection of Privately Held Natural Lands* (Philadelphia: Natural Lands Trust, Inc., 1982).

Conservation easements usually involve either (*a*) the purchase by a government agency or nonprofit organization of the right to build upon a parcel of land or (*b*) the donation of that right by the property owner. Such arrangements allow land to remain in private ownership and on the tax rolls. They also permit the continuation of existing land uses, including farming, that are compatible with river conservation objectives, while controlling any future land-use changes. Easements, however, may be of limited duration and may not provide for public access. They generally cost less than total purchase of a property, but the difference is sometimes small.

Voluntary Agreements

Voluntary agreements may be drawn up to conserve privately owned agricultural land, large forest areas, utility right-of-way corridors, and land owned or administered by private nonprofit organizations or public agencies. These agreements may allow for controlled public access to the land and are granted for a specified period of time. Generally, however, they can be terminated at the will of the private landowner. A recent example

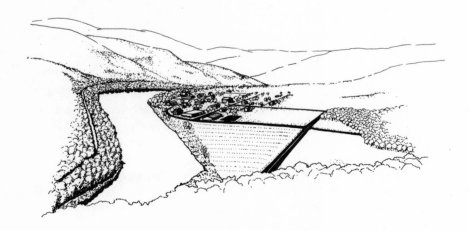

of a voluntary agreement is a cooperative arrangement made between the Great Northern Paper Company and the state of Maine in 1981. In that arrangement, Great Northern agreed to provide for public-recreation access along a portion of the West Branch of the Penobscot River and to limit forest cutting near the river's corridor.

Land Purchases

The absolute ownership of a parcel of land and any building on it (known as full-fee, or fee-simple, ownership) can be transferred by purchase, exchange, or donation. Total ownership of property can be costly, but it does carry with it the ability to control all uses of the land and to allow or forbid access to the public. This conservation tool usually is recommended for property that has particularly high preservation value or is intended for public recreation. Public agencies have long used land purchase as a primary approach to acquiring control of land. In recent years, it has been used increasingly by private land trusts, such as the Nature Conservancy and the Trust for Public Land, which have become popular and effective organizations for acquiring and managing land to conserve it. (Two such land trusts, the Brandywine Conservancy in Pennsylvania and the Yakima River Greenway in Washington State, are discussed in chapter 4.)

Tax Incentives

Tax incentives offer reductions in property or income taxes to landowners who forego development of their land or donate the control or ownership of it to a conservation agency or organization. The land, however, must have been officially identified (for example, in a river conservation plan) as having public conservation value to qualify for federal tax benefits.

Tax incentives, commonly in the form of deductions that can be subtracted from one's taxes, have been particularly successful in encouraging the donation or "bargain sale" of important natural areas to land trusts and in promoting the commercial rehabilitation of historic buildings. Similarly, landowners who donate easements or development rights to their lands may be able to take advantage of these incentives.

Another tax approach is preferential assessment, under which land that is being taxed at its highest market or potential-use value can be taxed at a much lower rate if its use is limited to prescribed functions that have conservation value (for example, agriculture or forestry). Preferential assessments can lessen the pressure on landowners, particularly farmers, to sell riverfront land for development. Sometimes an owner can receive preferential assessments by attaching restrictions onto the deed for a piece of property. These arrangements bind not just the present owner of a property but any future owners as well. (A tax-incentive conservation program in Oregon that encourages rural landowners to help restore streamside vegetation along their property is discussed in chapter 4.)

Zoning Ordinances

Zoning is the most widely used land-use tool available to local governments. State governments also have zoning authority. Zoning ordinances divide a community into districts in which specific land uses are permitted or excluded. In addition, they can set density limits for new construction within those districts. Zoning regulations can be useful in maintaining existing land uses that are compatible with river conservation objectives and in prohibiting land uses that are incompatible. Zoning is subject to constitutional limitations, however, and exceptions to zoning standards can be made by local zoning authorities. (Two river conservation programs in which zoning regulations have been used successfully, for the Saco River in Maine and the Upper Mississippi River in Minnesota, are described in chapter 4.)

Three examples of zoning controls that can be useful in river conservation planning are:

- *Floodplain zoning.* In most river areas, the identified 50- or 100-year floodplain (an area historically subject to flooding at least once every 50 or 100 years) would be zoned free from new development and filling, thereby significantly limiting the damage caused by periodic flooding. Communities

must regulate floodplains to be eligible for protection under the federally sponsored National Flood Insurance program.

- *Cluster development.* Subdivision regulations can require that residential units be clustered on limited-size lots so that larger open areas are created within new developments. This concept can be used to concentrate new construction on sites that are the most physically suitable for development, leaving other more scenic and less developable sites, such as wetlands or steep hills, in a natural state.
- *Special districts.* Governments can designate specifically defined areas (for example, historic districts or aquifer

recharge areas) in which special land-use provisions are required to conserve noteworthy characteristics. These land-
use provisions might limit new development or establish
strict standards for any new construction or modification
of existing structures.

Government Permitting

Virtually all major water projects on rivers, such as diversions
and dams, require permits issued by different federal and state
regulatory agencies. Another important conservation tool is your
ability, guaranteed under law, to participate or intervene in the
permitting process for these types of projects and to make your
interests known before a decision is made.

When you learn of a water project on a local river, you should
check promptly to see whether a government agency (especially
the U.S. Army Corps of Engineers) is directly involved or has
regulatory jurisdiction. The applicable agency should then be contacted immediately to let it know of your concerns and to determine the proper procedures for participating in the decision-
making process. You should also alert other state and federal
agencies, such as the U.S. Fish and Wildlife Service, that might
be interested.

Although procedures vary from agency to agency, depending
on the type of project involved, those for hydropower projects are
particularly important and illustrate generally how such proceedings work.*

Under the Federal Power Act, every proposed hydroelectric
project that is to be built on federal land or a navigable stream,
or that would feed electricity into interstate power systems, must
be approved by the Federal Energy Regulatory Commission
(FERC). A developer first files a preliminary permit application
with the FERC containing such information as engineering

---

* For a more detailed discussion of this issue, see Pete Vilbig, "The Dam-
ming of America," *Canoe* (March 1982), p. 43, and Stephen Burke, "Small
Scale Hydroelectric Development and Federal Environmental Law," *Boston
College Environmental Affairs Law Review*, vol. 9, no. 4 (1981-82), p. 815.

details, maps, and cost estimates. Notice is given in local papers and to other federal agencies such as the Fish and Wildlife Service. Citizens can formally intervene at this point, which gives you the right to receive and review documents and to take part in hearings and informal negotiations.

A preliminary permit is usually granted by the FERC but does not allow construction to begin. The permit authorizes the applicant to begin a dam feasibility study, which may take several years to complete. As part of this study, some type of environmental impact statement usually is required.

Once this preliminary work is completed, the developer files a license application containing all feasibility studies and environmental reports. Based on this material, the FERC conducts formal hearings to decide whether it is in the public interest for the project to be built. You can also participate in this formal phase of licensing, but you must file a second petition to intervene. Generally, a lawyer is necessary to provide adequate representation. And, if the FERC does issue a permit that is not satisfactory to river conservation interests, and if you have been a formal intervenor, you can ask the FERC to reconsider. If you still are not satisfied, you can then appeal the decision to a federal district court.

4. Choosing a Strategy

Once your basic organizing work is complete and you understand the river conservation issues relevant to your effort, the choice of a conservation strategy is your next critical decision. You must select an approach that is carefully matched to your capabilities and depth of support. Keep in mind what kinds of help might be available from different levels of government. Also, consider the economic environment of your region, precedents set by conservation actions (if any), and anticipated opposition. In the 1980s, new options and partnerships for river conservation are being created, as federal initiatives in river conservation continue a decline that began more than a decade ago. State and local governments, and private conservation organizations and land trusts, are assuming greater responsibility for the conservation of rivers.

The programs described in this chapter have been relatively successful at conserving river resources — but often through much trial and error.* As much can be learned from the processes described here as from the final outcomes of any of the programs. In several cases, successful river conservation efforts have employed a combination of approaches, perhaps involving different levels of government at different stages of the project.

---

* Contents for the case studies described in this chapter are listed in appendix D.

One strategy can give way to another.

Appropriate timing is frequently the key to success. As many river conservation programs have failed due to "too much, too soon" as to "too little, too late."

Private Nonprofit Conservation Action

There are several different ways that local citizen groups can organize to promote effective river conservation. Some groups concentrate on monitoring river developments or educating the public; still others get involved directly through purchasing land along a river.

One approach to private river conservation is the formation of river valley associations, membership organizations typically organized as private corporations to conserve and enhance the natural qualities of a specific river and its tributaries. Because these associations are nonprofit, they are eligible for foundation grants and can more easily encourage private donations.

River valley associations are not limited by political boundaries, so they can address issues throughout an entire watershed area and help define overall conservation priorities for a river. They can also represent a variety of different river interests and can coordinate and focus on those interests. Larger associations typically employ professional staffs with expertise on river issues who can closely monitor all developments that might affect the river and the organization's membership. Many associations publish newsletters as a way to keep river-area residents informed and involved.

Land trusts are another type of private organization that can play an important role in conserving river corridor resources. Generally speaking, these associations seek to conserve natural, agricultural, and historical resources by acquiring property interests in areas threatened with development. Land trusts use their nonprofit status to obtain below-market-value sales of property or, like river valley associations, tax-deductible donations.

In many instances, these trusts acquire easements that allow a landowner to continue using a parcel of property in some fashion, while preventing the land from being further developed.

The landowner may get a reduced property tax assessment and, in cases of clear public benefit, may take a charitable-donation deduction on his or her income tax, while the trust achieves its goal of conservation at less cost than full-fee purchase. Often, when a trust does acquire full title to some land, it subsequently resells the property to a public agency (a "rollover" purchase). Since many public agencies must pay fair market value for land purchases when exercising their powers of eminent domain, a land trust's ability to acquire land at below-market prices can result in substantial savings to government. The trust, meanwhile, can use funds from rollover transactions to purchase or acquire easements on additional threatened property. To date, approximately 500 private land trusts in the United States have preserved close to three million acres — an amount of land nearly the size of Connecticut.*

The Housatonic Valley Association

The Housatonic Valley Association (HVA) was founded as a non-profit corporation to promote the conservation of the Housatonic River Valley's natural environment, from the Massachusetts-Connecticut border to Long Island Sound. The primary geographical area of HVA's concern is over 80 miles long and includes 45 townships in Connecticut. A membership organization, HVA generates most of its income through donations.

Like many other watershed organizations in New England, HVA has for many years concentrated its attention on water-quality issues and river "greenway" planning. Most of its activities have focused on educating the public. Its Watershed Ed Program has helped regional secondary schools to start and continue programs in developing environmental knowledge through such projects as testing the chemical, physical, and biological properties of water bodies in adopted watershed areas. The Valley Watch Program has been responsible for reviewing and commenting

---

* Information on local and regional land trusts throughout the United States is available from the Land Trust Exchange, Mount Desert, Maine 04660. This organization publishes a very useful technical newsletter.

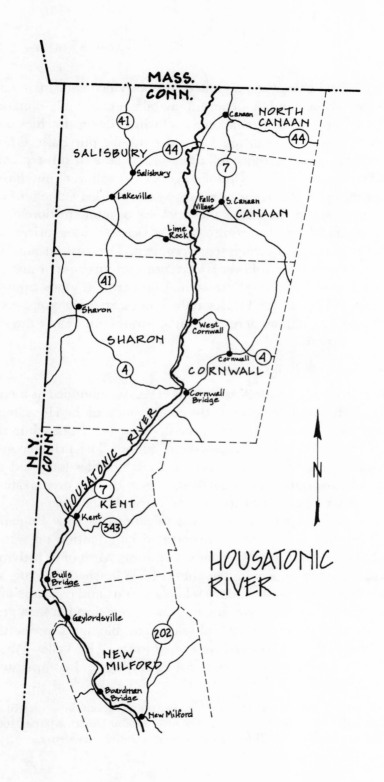

on several river-related projects, including sand and gravel extraction proposals and subdivision plans, and has prepared and presented testimony on basinwide surface- and groundwater classifications. Like many watershed associations, HVA publishes a quarterly newsletter and has produced additional pamphlets on polychlorinated biphenyls (PCBs) in the river, land conservation tools, and other subjects.

HVA has recently broken some new ground as a watershed association by forming a subsidiary regional land trust, the Housatonic Land Preservation Trust, thereby substantially increasing its ability to provide technical services to towns, organizations, or individuals with specific land-use needs. As a part of this effort, HVA has begun to do estate planning, using staff skills in tax law, site analysis, resource management, and landscape architecture. Through this kind of activity, HVA can help to resolve potential land-use conflicts. It also can develop comprehensive land-management strategies that help landowners plan for their economic futures while maximizing conservation opportunities (for example, through easements for wetland or prime farmland). Moreover, this type of work may provide a continuing source of revenue for the organization. The preservation trust also is actively encouraging (and in several cases helping) Connecticut towns within the Housatonic watershed to update their town plans so that the plans require maintaining existing community open space, such as farmland or floodplain.

In addition to its activities through the Housatonic Land Preservation Trust, HVA offers training and assistance for other local land trusts. And HVA has taken the lead in creating the Connecticut Farmland Coalition, a statewide group pressing for a permanent state program for purchasing development rights on key agricultural land.

HVA has demonstrated an ability to address actively a wide range of environmental concerns in the Housatonic Valley, from farmland preservation to hazardous-waste disposal. By developing innovative approaches (such as Valley Watch and Watershed Ed) for involving river communities in these issues, HVA not only has significantly expanded people's awareness of the river's resources and condition, but also has served as an important catalyst for greater public involvement in the regional decision-making process. At the same time HVA has remained sufficiently flexible to respond to the concerns of individual landowners along the river.

The Brandywine Conservancy

The Brandywine Conservancy is a successful and relatively large land trust that broadened its initial focus on conserving a specific stretch of river corridor into a comprehensive approach to natural and cultural resource conservation. Located in eastern Pennsylvania, the Brandywine Conservancy was founded in 1967 in response to a proposed industrial park in Chadds Ford, along the Brandywine River. This proposal would have affected the "artistic corridor," a stretch of the Brandywine that was a favorite subject for the illustrator Howard Pyle and his students, many of whom (notably Andrew Wyeth) later became important American artists.

The Brandywine Conservancy's initial protection strategy resulted in full-fee purchase acquisition of the land slated for development of the industrial park. However, the conservancy soon dropped the primarily full-fee approach because of its high cost and began acquiring easements instead. By the end of 1981, the conservancy had acquired easements on more than 3,400 acres and fee-simple ownership on another 300 acres.

In the early 1970s, the conservancy conducted a comprehensive water-quality study of the river area and subsequently expanded its program to encompass protection of the Brandywine's tributaries and wetlands, as well as groundwater management. The conservancy also has established an ambitious Environmental Management Assistance Program, which helps local governments draft and implement land-use regulations and plans that assure protection of natural and historical resources. The program has included the preparation of a comprehensive handbook covering 16 areas of land-use and environmental law (updated regularly) and offered technical assistance to local governments, private land trusts, and other conservation organizations.

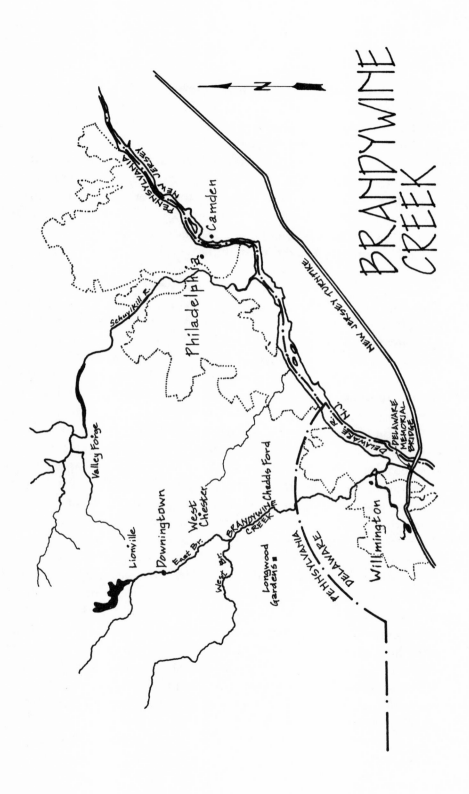

More recently, the Brandywine Conservancy has been involved in a study inventorying the natural and cultural features (for example, water-quality characteristics, land-use patterns, and historic features) of the West Branch of the Brandywine. The study is intended to support designation of the waterway as a scenic river under Pennsylvania's Scenic Rivers Act, thereby increasing state protection afforded the river. Affected local governments are participating in the study, which should result in a proposed management plan to guide private and government planning and decision making.

The Yakima River Greenway

The Yakima River Greenway in central Washington State perhaps provides a more typical example of the role that private land trusts play in river conservation, at least insofar as the scale and scope of its activities are concerned. It also illustrates how private land trusts can supplement government action and how local land trusts can benefit from the expertise of larger, more established trusts.

Central Washington is arid territory. Yakima is an agricultural community dependent on irrigation for its economic well-being, so the Yakima River, which flows east of the city, is important to the area's residents. Because Yakima developed along a railroad line one and one-half miles west of the Yakima River, rather than along the river itself, development pressure on the river corridor did not really begin until the 1960s, when an interstate highway was built between the town and the river. Yakima residents were thus presented with a rare opportunity to conserve a high-quality waterfront that did not need extensive cleanup or restoration. In the mid-1960s, the Washington State legislature funded development of a comprehensive master plan for a nine-mile stretch of the river. Completed in 1977, the plan envisioned the creation of a 3,600-acre "greenway" along both sides of the Yakima River. Approximately 1,600 acres of the proposed greenway were in public ownership, but much of this public land was not dedicated to public recreation.

YAKIMA RIVER

The comprehensive plan, however, lacked any implementation mechanism. Its recommendations languished until 1979, when the county appointed a task force to study the feasibility of implementing the plan. The task force recommended, and the county adopted, the establishment of a private, local land trust to acquire the land. The trust was to utilize the expertise and resources of the San Francisco-based Trust for Public Land (TPL). With TPL's active involvement, the Yakima River Greenway Foundation was soon incorporated. TPL agreed to hold donated parcels and easements until the greenway received nonprofit status from the Internal Revenue Service. The greenway received that status in the spring of 1981, slightly more than a year after its incorporation, and TPL transferred to the greenway the deeds to the two parcels it had been holding.

The greenway encompasses three distinct stretches of the Yakima River. According to the comprehensive plans the northern and southern stretches of the greenway will be left undeveloped. The western side of the middle stretch will be extensively developed as a public park and arboretum. Park development will include reclaiming an abandoned four-acre garbage dump, as well as a gravel mine after it closes down its operations. Finally, an existing state park on the eastern side of the middle stretch will be expanded.

The greenway foundation is still in the early stages of its development. To date, it has concentrated its efforts mainly on fund-raising. It has acquired about 75 acres and has raised approximately $440,000 toward establishing an $80,000 annual maintenance trust fund and developing the river's middle stretch. The foundation intends to focus its effort on the most degraded and threatened areas of the Yakima; it does not want to acquire all of the private land in the greenway, since some of that land is adequately protected by floodplain zoning. The foundation expects to "roll over" to the local government much of the private property it acquires, continuing the extensive cooperation between the city, the county, and the foundation that has characterized this project from its inception.

River Corridor Commissions and Local Land-Use Planning

A river corridor commission usually consists of representatives from neighboring municipal or county governments who have entered into a cooperative association to conserve a segment of river frontage that crosses their political boundaries. The objective of such a commission is to bring together communities dependent on river resources and to develop mutually acceptable and enforceable standards for land use along the river. The commission approach is based on the principle that, since a river does not recognize political boundaries, its resources are shared by all and can therefore only be conserved by a cooperative effort.

A river corridor commission can be created by intermunicipal agreement, or a state legislature can establish and empower one as a regulatory agency. Some commissions are primarily advisory, setting up guidelines for the voluntary compliance of participating governments. Other commissions exercise zoning authority or have participating towns adopt special uniform land-use and planning ordinances.

The advantage of the commission approach to river conservation is that it recognizes the political importance of home rule and decision making by citizens who share at least some common values and concerns. A commission can act with the credibility of representing locally elected governments, something a state or federal regulatory agency does not have. In principle, a commission is also more sensitive to local needs.

The major disadvantage, however, is the difficulty of establishing such a commission. Local units of government may find it hard to identify shared interests and common priorities. Since much of the work of local government is done on a voluntary basis, the staff time and resources needed for participation may be in short supply. In addition, there may be little or no precedent for cooperative efforts beyond individual village or county boundaries. Another disadvantage is that, where commissions are established on the basis of voluntary compliance by participating towns, the enforcement of standards is often arbitrary. This is particularly true in situations where towns are vulnerable to pressure from a large riverfront landowner. In some cases, these problems can be offset with the assistance of a strong citizens organization and with technical assistance and subsidies from higher levels of government.

Two examples of river commissions that have overcome many obstacles are the Saco River Corridor Commission in Maine and the Mississippi Headwaters Board in Minnesota. Although river conservationists in other parts of the United States may not be able to replicate these two programs exactly, many of the factors contributing to their success can — and should — be used elsewhere.

The Saco River Corridor Commission

The Saco River flows from the White Mountains of New Hampshire through the coniferous forests and dairy farms of Maine out to Saco Bay on the Atlantic near Portland. Eighty-four miles of the river are in Maine. The Saco supplies the water for 40,000 local residents and a summer population of nearly 100,000.

In the 1960s, a citizens group, the Saco River Corridor Association (SRCA), was formed by people along the Saco who were concerned over plans for large-scale residential development on the predominantly rural river. The SRCA played a key role in convincing the Maine legislature to support a regional planning effort for the future of the Saco valley.

In 1971, a plan was prepared that could enable local river towns to utilize a uniform system of zoning ordinances to guide changes in land use within the immediate area of the river. The Maine legislature approved the plan in 1973 and established the Saco River Corridor Commission (SRCC), composed of one appointee from each of the 20 municipalities in the river corridor. Since 1973, the commission membership has included teachers, farmers, truck drivers, lawyers, homemakers, a mechanic, and retirees.

The legislature directed the commission to develop a system of land-use regulations that would prevent new activities along the river that were potentially harmful to the Saco's water quality and amenities. In response, the commission created three land-

Fryburg
Kezar Pond
Lovewell Pond
Brown-field
NEW HAMPSHIRE
MAINE
Cornish
SACO
East Limington
RIVER
Portland
Saco
Biddiford
Sanford
Kennybunk
ATLANTIC OCEAN
N
Kittery
Portsmouth

SACO RIVER

use districts where certain activities now require permit review.

One, the Resource Protection District, comprises around 40 percent of the river corridor. Areas where the entire width of the corridor is within the 100-year floodplain are included in the district, as are wetlands, important wildlife habitat, and lands that have been designated by landowners for inclusion in the district. This district is used primarily for farming and forestry; new industrial or commercial development within it is discouraged, although existing nonconforming uses are allowed to remain in place.

More than half of the corridor is within a second area, a Limited Residential District, where the predominant use is "low-density residential." Within this area, the commission uses an aggregate system to encourage a variety of lot sizes and building locations and thereby minimize the visual impact of conventional subdivisions. Under this system, any newly developed lot must have at least 100 feet of river frontage, and its river frontage and setback distances together must total at least 500 feet. In addition, nothing can be built within the 100-year floodplain.

The remainder of the corridor is a General Development District, containing those lands already intensively used before the establishment of the commission. Permits are required in this district only for new industrial activities, including any sand or topsoil mining.

The SRCC reviews about 50 permit applications a year. Its two paid staff members devote almost all their time to working with applicants on acceptable conditions for their permits; occasionally, the staff deals with enforcement problems. The commission operates on a $35,000 yearly budget, of which $10,000 comes from the state, the remainder from county government. (Commissioners themselves receive no compensation for their work.) Despite the commission's considerable success in implementing a land-use program and its ability to work closely with local landowners, it still struggles from year to year to secure a minimum operating budget. The small budget hinders the commission's ability to work closely with local planning boards and maintain the strong grass-roots citizen involvement that existed when the SRCC was first established. The commission has no planning capability and has difficulty responding to new river problems, such as the dramatic rise in recreational canoeing and related management needs. In fact, management of canoeists is the greatest unmet challenge on the Saco today.

Despite these shortcomings, the SRCC remains one of the few examples of cooperative home-rule river conservation, where local towns recognize a river as a common resource and wrestle with the difficult trade-offs involved in protecting its most important qualities. Fortunately, the new Maine Rivers Act may increase state matching support for the commission and place its operation on a more secure financial footing for the future. (This act is discussed later in the chapter.)

The Mississippi Headwaters Board

In 1979, Congress directed the National Park Service to study 466 miles of the Upper Mississippi River for possible designation and management as a national wild and scenic river (this program is discussed later in this chapter). The Upper Mississippi begins its journey at Lake Itasca in northern Minnesota and flows south, toward the Twin Cities, through lakes, forests, and small towns. The river's course has also been marked by a growing number of pulp mill and municipal sewage outfalls, power plants, dams, and unplanned and poorly sited commercial and residential developments.

Residents of the region recognized the need to conserve the Upper Mississippi but wanted to do so without giving up local control. As an alternative to federal involvement, a proposal was made that local governments begin a joint effort to protect the river. In early 1980, representatives from six counties met and recommended that a joint powers board be formed to develop a river conservation plan. (Authority for such a board is provided in a Minnesota statute that permits local governments to cooperate in exercising any power held in common.)

Strong support for this approach existed among local elected

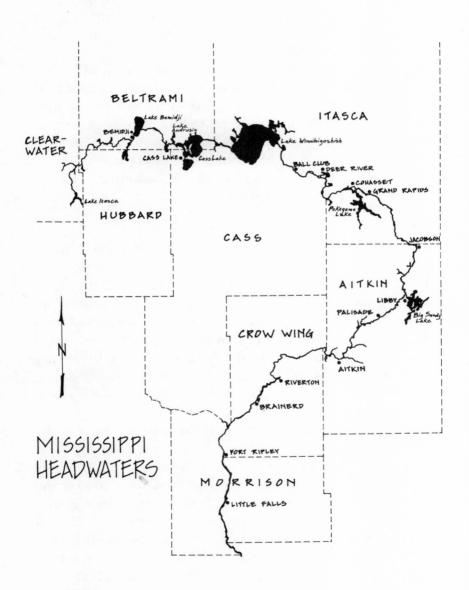

BELTRAMI

ITASCA

CLEAR-
WATER

Lake Bemidji

*Lake
Andrusia*

BEMIDJI

Lake Winnibigoshish

CASS LAKE   *Cass Lake*

BALL CLUB

DEER RIVER

COHASSET

GRAND RAPIDS

Lake Itasca

HUBBARD

*Pokegama
Lake*

CASS

JACOBSON

AITKIN

LIBBY

PALISADE

*Big Sandy
Lake*

CROW WING

N

AITKIN

RIVERTON

BRAINERD

FORT RIPLEY

MISSISSIPPI
HEADWATERS

MORRISON

LITTLE FALLS

representatives, civic leaders, and journalists. Officials of eight counties along the river soon signed a joint powers agreement creating the Mississippi Headwaters Board (MHB). The board, comprised of a county commissioner from each of the counties, was set up with the following objectives: to establish uniform zoning and land management guidelines, to apportion the cost of comprehensive planning among the participating counties, and to ensure that no single county board succumbed to special-interest pressure at the expense of the public welfare.

The first action of the Headwaters Board was the preparation, with the assistance of a consultant, of a comprehensive intergovernmental plan for the upper 400 miles of the river. The MHB formed a citizens advisory committee, including representatives of landowners, agriculture, labor, business, and conservation interests, as well as a technical advisory committee, which guided the preparation of the plan. The MHB plan addresses the adoption and administration of comprehensive land- and water-use ordinances to guide shoreline development; the management and improvement of recreational opportunities provided by the river; and the upgrading of public land management's ability to improve fish and wildlife habitat and the visual quality of the river corridor.

In addition, the board has prepared a model ordinance, establishing minimum standards for residential lot sizes (12- and 5-acre minimums), building setbacks, sewage system design and placement, and the cutting of vegetation. In the unlikely event that a county refuses to abide by the ordinance or withdraws from the compact, state legislation authorizes the Minnesota Department of Natural Resources to assume management of the affected river segment.

Well-staffed county governments provide critical in-kind services to the MHB. The board uses county zoning officers and attorneys, and the counties undertake any land acquisition and management responsibilities. In addition, the board continues to be well funded by the state, with a $91,000 grant for the MHB included in the Minnesota government's 1983-84 budget.

State River Conservation Programs

Approximately 25 state legislatures have enacted some type of legislation aimed at protecting rivers, but these actions to conserve rivers have had limited success. Until recently, most of these laws were patterned after the federal wild and scenic rivers program, with the intent of creating state systems of outstanding scenic riverways, protected by a combination of state-sponsored acquisition, zoning, and easements. However, few of these state programs have made substantial progress toward implementing their programs. Instead, many of them, after an initial handful of studies or designations, have remained essentially inactive for nearly a decade. Many reasons have been offered for this situation: lack of public involvement (particularly by landowners along a waterway) in river designations and management planning; difficulty in coordinating programs with other state agencies and development priorities; overreliance on state regulatory authority; and reluctance by state governments to place a high enough priority on river programs. In addition, the Federal Energy Regulatory Commission (FERC) has refused to comply with state prohibitions on water development projects on scenic rivers.

In response to these difficulties, several states have been rethinking their involvement with river conservation and have developed new directions for conserving their rivers. Three of these approaches are described here: comprehensive river resource planning in Maine, programs to help local conservation projects that complement state efforts in Massachusetts, and tax incentives in Oregon.

Maine's Comprehensive Approach

The state of Maine recently completed an extensive effort to identify and protect its most significant rivers and to provide a rational framework for the management of all river and stream resources in the state. These actions were largely precipitated by a dramatic increase in requests for hydropower-development permits, but the Maine government was also responding to a public

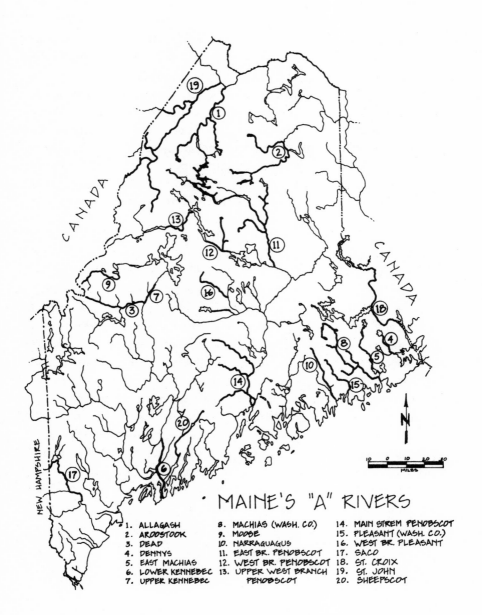

MAINE'S "A" RIVERS

1. ALLAGASH
2. AROOSTOOK
3. DEAD
4. DENNYS
5. EAST MACHIAS
6. LOWER KENNEBEC
7. UPPER KENNEBEC

8. MACHIAS (WASH. CO.)
9. MOOSE
10. NARRAGUAGUS
11. EAST BR. PENOBSCOT
12. WEST BR. PENOBSCOT
13. UPPER WEST BRANCH
    PENOBSCOT

14. MAIN STREM PENOBSCOT
15. PLEASANT (WASH. CO.)
16. WEST BR. PLEASANT
17. SACO
18. ST. CROIX
19. ST. JOHN
20. SHEEPSCOT

perception that rivers are vital to the state's quality of life and its cultural heritage.

Maine's river resources have long been an essential ingredient in the state's cultural and economic development. All major settlements in the state were founded next to the Kennebec and Penobscot rivers. These rivers soon became conduits for commercial and industrial growth as they carried goods and timber, provided power for manufacturing, contributed to the fishing industry, and even provided the raw product for the 19th-century ice trade with China. Eventually, however, deteriorating water quality forced the state's residents to abandon the rivers. This situation, combined with changing transportation technology and a decreased demand for water as a power source, drastically altered the mid-20th-century Maine resident's perception of rivers and river values.

The last 15 years have seen a rejuvenated interest in Maine's rivers. The renewed concern was initiated by state and federal water-quality efforts and then fueled by increased calls for hydropower, heightened interest in fisheries restoration and outdoor recreation, and growing demand for shorefront residential and recreational development. Confronted with a growing need for a policy addressing competing river uses, state officials undertook a comprehensive inventory and assessment of natural and recreational values associated with rivers, through a cooperative study by the Maine Department of Conservation and the National Park Service. The Maine Rivers Study collected natural, physical, and recreational resource information in categories such as "anadromous fisheries," "geologic-hydrologic," "cultural-historic," and "whitewater boating." In addition, shoreline development was analyzed to identify significant "undeveloped river" segments. This information was combined with the views of resource experts, river users, conservation groups, and other interested people to assemble a comprehensive resource inventory for 3,200 miles of rivers and streams. The study also identified conservation priorities that could be supported by a variety of previously uncoordinated river interests.

Through further public review, a consensus was reached on

the comparative significance of all state river resources and rivers and tributaries that should be recognized as the state's most outstanding natural and recreational resources. These river segments became known as Maine's "A" rivers. The assessment proved to be important in providing an objective foundation for future policy decisions. In addition, the extensive public involvement at each stage of the study helped create a wide-ranging network of interested citizens that soon coalesced into an effective river conservation constituency.

The public consensus motivated the state's lawmakers to take action. Governor Joseph Brennan issued an executive order designating the 20 most outstanding rivers identified in the study as resources that merited special consideration and declaring that no new dams were to be constructed on those segments. Two locations where the state had made prior commitments were excluded from the order.

Three important actions followed. The Maine Office of Energy Resources developed a comprehensive hydroelectric plan detailing how future hydropower capacity could be developed through the year 2000 while protecting the river stretches covered by the governor's order. In an effort to keep federal programs consistent with state conservation efforts, this plan — along with the Maine Rivers Study and the executive order — has been forwarded to the FERC.

Concurrently with the development of the energy plan, the state planning office completed an assessment of existing river protection mechanisms and made a series of recommendations that became the basis for the Maine Rivers Act, signed into law by Governor Brennan in 1983. The act prohibits the state licensing of new dams on nearly 1,000 miles of 16 outstanding river segments and streamlines the existing state hydropower-permitting process. The act also strengthens shoreline zoning standards and subdivision setbacks adjacent to these river segments and provides for matching funds for river corridor commissions. Additional planning is authorized for fishery management and recreation access.

At the same time that these legislative developments were occurring, another state action with far-reaching implications took place. The Land Use Regulation Commission, the state agency empowered to regulate development in Maine's unincorporated townships, initiated zoning changes for rivers that were under its jurisdiction and merited special consideration according to the executive order. These changes were intended to affect development, roads, gravel extraction, and timber harvesting within a 250-foot-wide corridor along each side of a designated river.

Not everyone in Maine agreed with the comprehensive approach to river conservation. Some people felt that the state program, with its emphasis on setting priorities and encouraging compatible corridor development, would result in "trading off" valuable river areas that had not made the "A" list. Some citizens in rural areas complained that state actions were not responsive to their local development needs and noted that additional state land-use restrictions would unfairly penalize depressed rural communities near most of the outstanding river segments.

There is no question that the Maine rivers program involved compromise and some significant trade-offs. But it is also clear that a comprehensive framework now exists for conserving Maine's river resources for many years to come. Moreover, the experience in Maine has provided useful ideas for river conservation work in other parts of the country:

- An objective and widely accepted assessment of resources can serve as a solid foundation for future action.
- Extensive public involvement in the study process increases credibility and promotes the development of a broad base of support.
- Public consensus on conservation priorities can create a political climate favorable to a wide range of conservation actions.
- To be successful, a large-scale river conservation effort requires considerable long-term commitment and expertise as well as close coordination between public and private sectors.

- The advocacy of balanced programs, with a focus on conflict avoidance, will broaden the political support base for conservation actions.
- Integrating action into existing institutions and legal mechanisms often is preferable to inventing totally new programs.

Massachusetts's Scenic Rivers Program

In 1971, the Massachusetts legislature passed a Scenic and Recreational Rivers Act to classify and conserve the state's outstanding natural, cultural, and recreational rivers and streams. A Scenic Rivers Program was established within the Massachusetts Department of Environmental Management (DEM), and a comprehensive inventory of all state rivers was completed, proposing some 50 rural and urban rivers and river segments for designation.

Area legislators, local officials, landowners, and citizen advisory committees play an important role in the designation process. Before a river is officially designated into the statewide system, a protective order and management plan must be developed and adopted by the DEM commissioner. The protective orders regulate activities such as dredging or filling within 100 yards of a river's natural bank and are recorded on the deeds of riverfront landowners. As of early 1984, three rivers, a total of 24 river miles, had been designated as "state scenic rivers."

Because this state-level designation process was found to be both expensive and time-consuming, the original legislative authority has been de-emphasized during the last five years, and several innovative approaches to river conservation, which stress local initiative, have been developed. Rivers with state-approved but locally developed and supported conservation mechanisms or management plans can be officially recognized as "local scenic rivers" if those plans outline specific conservation strategies. The Scenic Rivers Program can offer technical assistance and, in some cases, funding to communities to help them develop these strategies. These river corridors receive priority for state grants and, if requested, additional state protection is available. Although local scenic designation alone does not guarantee the conservation of important river resources, the planning process can pull together local and state agencies to improve zoning, enforce existing land-use regulations, and suggest selective acquisition of sites with critical conservation or recreational value. To date, there are two local scenic rivers covering approximately 62 river miles in Massachusetts.

In a related effort, begun in 1980, DEM and the Scenic Rivers Program initiated a program to provide funding for local water-shed associations performing "greenway" planning along rivers that had been recommended for designation as state scenic rivers. Originally, this "greenway" program used outdoor recreational planning moneys from the federal Land and Water Conservation Fund, though it is now financed entirely by the state. Proposals are evaluated on a competitive basis, and DEM annually awards two grants of between $10,000 and $15,000 to local non-profit organizations. These awards require 25 to 50 percent matching funding from the applicant, and $20,000 is considered a minimum project budget. The program has proven to be a cat-alyst for major river conservation efforts in the watersheds where awards have been made and helped inspire the recent passage by the state legislature of an acquisition bond that earmarked $24.5 million for river corridors.

The Massachusetts Scenic Rivers Program is now recognized for its comprehensiveness and its local citizen participation. Reorienting the program to encourage local initiative and pro-viding technical and financial assistance to responsive com-munities has created a growing state and local partnership in river conservation.

Oregon's Riparian Tax Incentive Program

In 1981, the Oregon legislature established a two-pronged Riparian Tax Incentive Program, administered by the state's Department of Fish and Wildlife, to maintain or enhance stream-side areas and improve instream fish habitat. The narrow cor-ridors of land adjacent to rivers or streams (known as riparian zones) are very important to Oregon's fish and wildlife. For example, more than 75 percent of the wildlife species in the southeastern portion of the state rely on such habitat to survive. Fish also depend on good riparian land since bankside vegetation buffers a stream's water temperature and keeps sediment from being washed into the waterway.

The first prong of Oregon's program grants a complete property tax exemption for eligible lands. A participating landowner pays no property tax on a streambed or lands within 100 feet of the stream's channel, if these lands are already zoned by a county land-use plan as either woodland or agricultural, including rangeland. The landowner must implement a Cooperative Management Agreement, which clearly states that only land-use activities consistent with the protection or restoration of riparian habitat will be permitted along the stream corridor. This incentive essentially functions as an easement: a landowner limits adverse land-use practices, such as grazing livestock down to the water's edge, in exchange for a property tax exemption for the affected area.

The second prong of Oregon's program provides an income tax credit for certified fish-habitat improvement projects. Up to 25 percent of the cost incurred in a project (for example, bank stabilization or fencing) can be deducted from one's personal or corporate state income tax.

Both portions of the Oregon program are voluntary, relying on public-private cooperation. Participation by landowners in either one does not, in itself, grant public access to private property.

The program does have its limitations. The state legislature has restricted both the number of miles of eligible stream bank and the total tax credit allowed for the program in any given year. In addition, despite the monetary inducements, the basic thrust of the program is educational. A property tax exemption for two miles of stream frontage, 100 feet deep, usually will not cover the cost of two miles of new fencing. It is not surprising, therefore, that applications have been slow to come in. However, the tax-relief approach does help to draw attention to the program and its other more long-term benefits for landowners, such as controlling soil erosion and maintaining the water-storage capacity of the riparian zone, which improves stream flow in the late summer. And because the program is voluntary, state officials now have a basis for working one-on-one with riparian landowners in a friendly, nonthreatening way.

National Wild and Scenic River System

In 1968, Congress decided that established federal policies of building dams, levees, and diversions along rivers should be complemented by a policy that preserved outstanding free-flowing stretches of the nation's waterways. These selected river segments would form the National Wild and Scenic River System. The National Wild and Scenic Rivers Act created a procedure by which river segments across the country could be evaluated and then designated as a component of the system.*

Once a river is placed into the National Wild and Scenic River System by Congress, either the National Park Service (NPS) or the U.S. Forest Service (USFS) usually is given the responsibility to ensure that the special qualities of the river are never lost or seriously degraded. No federal agency can then approve (through licensing) or assist by any other means the construction of water-resource projects (including dams and diversions) that might adversely affect a designated river segment. Since all water-resource projects require federal licensing, this part of the National Wild and Scenic Rivers Act effectively guarantees that these river segments will remain free-flowing. Federally funded or approved projects such as highways and power transmission lines fall under similar restrictions.

Designated river segments are classified as "Wild," "Scenic," or "Recreational" on the basis of how much development is already along their banks. The act directs that, for each river segment added to the system, a management plan be prepared identifying important river features and proposing a long-term strategy for their conservation.

---

* Appendix E lists waterways included in the National Wild and Scenic River System.

River segments usually are added to the system directly by Congress, under Section 5(a) of the National Wild and Scenic Rivers Act, but they can be added at a state's request under Section 2(a)(ii), subject to the secretary of the interior's approval, if the designation does not entail federal cost. States may use this alternative to ensure protection from federally funded or licensed water projects while still maintaining state and local control and management responsibility.

In addition, states can increase their coordination with federal river conservation programs by petitioning the secretary to designate a waterway as a "Section 5(d) river." This section of the act stipulates:

> In all planning for the use and development of water and related land resources, consideration shall be given by all federal agencies involved to potential national wild, scenic and recreational river areas, and all river basin and project plan reports submitted to the Congress shall consider and discuss any such potentials. The Secretary of the Interior and the Secretary of Agriculture shall make specific studies and investigations to determine which additional wild, scenic and recreational river areas within the United States shall be evaluated in planning reports by all federal agencies as potential alternative uses of the water and related land resources involved.

Today there are 61 river segments included in the national system, or a total of 6,900 river miles in 23 states. Almost two-thirds of these rivers are located in the western states, including Alaska. The Alaska National Interest Lands Conservation Act of 1980, which created special protection for large tracts of federally owned land in Alaska, nearly doubled the mileage of the system.

Most of the river segments first added to the system already flowed through largely undeveloped, federally managed land — usually USFS or Bureau of Land Management holdings. As a result, federal agencies responsible for their protection under the act had a relatively free hand in their management. However, once this precedent was established, it proved difficult to break, and designation of a waterway as a national wild and scenic river became synonymous with extensive federal landownership and tight management even along more populated river corridors that included state- or privately owned land. Not until the late 1970s did Congress amend the system to limit federal land acquisition and mandate a cooperative federal, state, and local conservation planning effort.

Long accustomed to federal predominance, NPS and USFS planners and managers often have not been sensitive enough to local sentiments and occasionally have acquired more land than was necessary to carry out their mission. This sometimes heavy-handed behavior has fueled a negative perception of the wild and scenic rivers program among some people, which, coupled with opposition from special interests, has taken its toll on the system. It has, importantly, hindered the system's expansion beyond the core group of western rivers. Of the 88 river segments identified by Congress since 1968 for study and potential inclusion in the system, only 14 have made it all the way to designation.

Despite these difficulties, there remains an advantage to having a waterway named as a national wild and scenic river: the protection against dams and other water projects offered by such a designation cannot be provided by other conservation mechanisms. For example, as has already been mentioned, state prohibitions on proposed water developments have not yet been formally recognized by the Federal Energy Regulatory Commission.

It has been noted that, if a state wishes to have one of its waterways added to the National Wild and Scenic River System, it can petition the secretary of the interior to designate the waterway as a 2(a)(ii) or 5(d) river. The state also can obtain federal coordination assistance from the NPS through the use of the Nationwide Rivers Inventory. This inventory, prepared in every state except Montana under the provision of Section 5(d) between 1976 and 1982, identifies rivers and river segments that are eligible for further study or inclusion in the system. In addition, rivers listed on the inventory are afforded the protections of a Council on Environmental Quality communiqué directing federal agencies that initiate or license a project to avoid or mitigate adverse effects on rivers identified in the inventory. Moreover, NPS regional offices use this directive and the federal environmental review process to avoid or minimize conflicts between conservation efforts and energy and water development projects.

In recent years, amendments to and reinterpretation of the National Wild and Scenic Rivers Act have begun to change the way the act is used to conserve rivers. The Upper Delaware National Wild and Scenic River, created in 1978, and the NPS's River Conservation Technical Assistance Program represent significant new approaches to river conservation by the federal government.

The Upper Delaware National Wild and Scenic River

The quiet, pastoral Upper Delaware region of southern New York and northern Pennsylvania is considered by many to be a unique "cultural landscape" evoking many scenic and life-style characteristics of the 19th century. This distinction is accentuated by the Upper Delaware River's proximity to major metropolitan centers; the heavily wooded river valley is only a two-hour drive from New York City. Most land along the river is privately owned, with much of it used for commercial timber harvesting.

The 75-mile stretch of river is very popular with canoeists and anglers, and, given the area's accessibility, the smaller communities along the river face many problems associated with heavy recreational use. Over the years, local residents have grown alarmed by littering and trespassing on their land, and their towns have been unable to pay for the increased trash removal and police protection that have become necessary.

In 1973, a congressionally authorized study of the Upper Delaware recommended that the river be included in the National Wild and Scenic River System. Over the next several years, support grew, particularly within the New York and Pennsylvania state governments, as well as in the congressional delegations from the two states, for some kind of federal role in conserving the Upper Delaware. Many local residents and public officials were wary of federal involvement, but they were unable to put together a workable regional or intermunicipal conservation alternative.

Instead, in 1978, new hybrid legislation was proposed by the area's members of Congress. Unlike anything that had preceded it, this legislation placed the Upper Delaware in the National Wild and Scenic River System, but with some very specific conditions. The NPS, it was stipulated, was to acquire no more than 1,450 of the 83,000 acres in the river corridor—less than 2 percent of the total area. The resources of the Upper Delaware were to be protected primarily through local land-use regulations, including comprehensive plans and zoning ordinances developed with federal assistance. These local standards were to be consistent with a new river-corridor management plan and would need the secretary of the interior's approval.

The legislation instructed the 15 towns along the river, their 5 counties, the Delaware River Basin Commission (a regional water-resource agency), the states of New York and Pennsylvania, and the NPS to develop cooperatively a plan to manage the corridor. State and county planning agencies were funded to participate with NPS in developing this plan, and a Citizen's Advisory Commission was appointed to guide its preparation. In addition, to provide immediate relief not just from existing recreational pressure but also from an anticipated increase in use, approximately $250,000 a year was allocated by Congress to the river towns on a contractual basis for expanded law enforcement and trash cleanup along the river.

As of early 1984, a draft management plan for the river had been prepared and was undergoing public review. It proposed licensing canoe-rental businesses and maintaining productive fisheries, as well as establishing an intergovernmental coordinating council to provide a forum for the different levels of government responsible for the river valley's conservation. Private land trusts were to be given an important role in preserving key landscape features along the river. In addition, the plan recommended that the NPS acquire only 156 acres of land, well under the legislative limit, primarily to provide river-access sites, a few campgrounds, and visitor-orientation centers.

Coordinating such a large planning effort has been a demanding, sometimes frustrating, experience for the NPS. The sheer size of the interagency planning team and the participants' occasional fluctuation on key issues has made consensus hard to achieve. It is still too early to judge the overall effectiveness of the Upper Delaware National Wild and Scenic River project. Hopefully, however, the NPS will learn much from its outcome. The project does clearly demonstrate that there can be flexibiity in crafting new types of wild and scenic rivers and that the National Wild and Scenic Rivers Act can be amended to provide federal protection of free-flowing rivers without necessarily sacrificing local responsibility and self-determination.

NPS River Conservation Technical Assistance

Section 11 of the National Wild and Scenic Rivers Act authorizes the National Park Service to assist local, state, and federal government agencies and private groups and landowners interested in developing river conservation plans. Upon request, each of the NPS's regional offices can provide this assistance, which is funded annually by Congress.*

The NPS assistance program is designed to emphasize the need for all levels of government and the private sector to work together in their efforts to conserve rivers. The program also recognizes the predominant desire by state and local governments to maintain home rule and the need for governments to be sensitive to the interests of private landowners. Local governments, private groups, and landowners are usually all given major roles when river conservation plans are developed, and NPS project recommendations try to reflect a consensus of all these participants.

Applications for assistance are accepted annually by the NPS, which evaluates them to determine their appropriateness for federal involvement. Three major criteria are considered by the NPS as it assesses potential projects:

- Projects should be cooperative efforts that are locally supported and politically feasible.
- Projects should include river areas listed on the Nationwide Rivers Inventory or other areas of national importance.
- Projects should be complex enough to warrant federal involvement.

---

* See Appendix A for a list of NPS regional offices, which also can supply you with a copy of the Nationwide Rivers Inventory for your area.

Assistance from the NPS generally focuses on: (*a*) assisting state agencies in the development of statewide river inventories and assessments, such as the one done in Maine; (*b*) developing cooperative plans for managing river corridors; (*c*) providing technical staff support to established state river programs on designated river segments; and (*d*) conducting case-study demonstration projects to develop strategies that rely on land-conservation tools other than full-fee ownership. Such projects generally take from six months to one year to complete and result in a report that documents the values of a river corridor and describes plans for its conservation.

The NPS river conservation assistance offers states and communities a better opportunity to form a partnership with the federal government to promote river conservation. The expertise and experience of the NPS is made available to the states, and a conservation program sensitive to local concerns and issues is guaranteed.

Conclusion

The conservation of rivers, like the natural and physical processes that created them, is a slow and time-consuming
business. Our rivers are a valuable and diminishing natural and
cultural resource. The competition between conservation and non-
conservation interests for these areas has never been greater and
can be expected to increase over the next decade.

Ironically, as the qualities of more and more American rivers
are diminished or destroyed, many federal and state conservation agencies and programs are being reduced and even elim-
inated. In response, people at the local government level and
within the private sector are realizing that they must take the
initiative and play a greater role in the future management and
use of their rivers. This local- and private-initiative approach to
conservation certainly is not new, but it does appear to represent a significant change of direction for many public agencies
and private organizations that traditionally have relied on federal
and state governments for river conservation work.

Past experience clearly indicates that support does exist for river
conservation projects, provided that they are sensitive to local
attitudes, issues, and concerns. As you work to conserve a river,
you must always remember the importance of understanding the
perspectives of others in your community, even though this effort
often may be complicated and require much patience and
perserverance. You should be cautious about looking for single

solutions, programs, or techniques, since no one approach is likely to conserve a river. The reduction of much federal and state management of (and assistance to) conservation work makes it increasingly important that new river conservation constituencies be developed and that consensuses for action on our rivers be built. We must combine our efforts, share responsibilities, and make existing government and private-sector organizations work more effectively for us if we wish to continue and improve river conservation in the United States.

Appendix A: National Park Service Regional Offices

Office	States Covered
Alaska Regional Office 540 W. Fifth Avenue, Room 202 Anchorage, AK 99501 (907) 271-4196	Alaska
Mid-Atlantic Regional Office 143 S. Third Street Philadelphia, PA 19106 (215) 597-7018	Delaware, Maryland, Pennsylvania, Virginia, West Virginia, excluding parks assigned to the National Capital Region
Midwest Regional Office 1709 Jackson Street Omaha, NE 68102 (402) 221-3448	Illinois, Indiana, Iowa, Kansas, Michigan, Minnesota, Missouri, Nebraska, Ohio, Wisconsin
National Capital Regional Office 1100 Ohio Drive, SW Washington, DC 20242 (202) 426-6700	District of Columbia, some units in Maryland, Virginia, and West Virginia

North Atlantic Regional Office
15 State Street
Boston, MA 02109
(617) 223-3793

Connecticut, Maine,
Massachusetts, New
Hampshire, New Jersey,
New York, Rhode Island,
Vermont

Pacific Northwest Regional
  Office
2001 Sixth Avenue
Seattle, WA 98121
(206) 442-4830

Idaho, Oregon, Washington

Rocky Mountain Regional
  Office
P.O. Box 25287
Denver, CO 80225
(303) 234-3095

Colorado, Montana, North
Dakota, South Dakota, Utah,
Wyoming

Southeast Regional Office
Richard B. Russell Federal
  Building & U.S. Courthouse
75 Spring Street, SW
Atlanta, GA 30303
(404) 221-4998

Alabama, Florida, Georgia,
Kentucky, Mississippi, North
Carolina, Puerto Rico, South
Carolina, Tennessee, U.S.
Virgin Islands

Southwest Regional Office
P.O. Box 728
Santa Fe, NM 87501
(505) 988-6375

Arkansas, Louisiana, New
Mexico, Oklahoma, Texas,
northeast corner of Arizona

Western Regional Office
Box 36063
450 Golden Gate Avenue
San Francisco, CA 94102
(415) 556-5186

California, Hawaii, Nevada,
most of Arizona

Appendix B: National River Conservation Organizations

American Rivers Conservation Council
323 Pennsylvania Avenue, SE
Washington, DC 20003
(202) 547-6900

Environmental Policy Institute
218 D Street, SE
Washington, DC 20003
(202) 544-2600

Friends of the Earth
1045 Sansome Street
San Francisco, CA 94111
(415) 433-7373

Izaak Walton League of America, Inc.
1701 N. Fort Myer Drive, Suite 1100
Arlington, VA 22209
(703) 528-1818

National Audubon Society
950 Third Avenue
New York, NY 10022
(212) 832-3200

National Parks and Conservation Association
1701 18th Street, NW
Washington, DC 20009
(202) 265-2717

National Wildlife Federation
1412 16th Street, NW
Washington, DC 20036
(202) 797-6800

Sierra Club
530 Bush Street
San Francisco, CA 94108
(415) 981-8634

Trout Unlimited
501 Church Street, NE
Vienna, VA 22180
(703) 281-1100

The Wildlife Society
5410 Grosvenor Lane
Bethesda, MD 20814
(301) 897-9770

Appendix C: State River Program Managers

Alabama

John Strickland
Director
Plans and Programs Division
Department of Conservation and Natural Resources
64 N. Union Street
Montgomery, AL 36130
(205) 832-6370

Alaska

Judy Marquez
Director
Division of Parks
Department of Natural Resources
619 Warehouse Avenue
Anchorage, AK 99501
(907) 264-2106

Arizona

Wayne L. Schuler
Assistant Director
Arizona Outdoor Recreation Coordinating Commission
1624 W. Adams, Room 101
Phoenix, AZ 85007
(602) 255-5013

Arkansas

Director
Arkansas Natural and Scenic Rivers Commission
Continental Building, Suite 500
Maine & Markham Streets
Little Rock, AR 72201
(501) 371-8134

California

James W. Burns
Assistant Secretary
California Resources Agency
1416 Ninth Street, Room 1311
Sacramento, CA 95814
(916) 445-3758

Colorado

Dan Meriman
Colorado Water Conservation Board
1313 Sherman Street
Denver, CO 80203
(303) 866-3441

Connecticut

Pamela Adams
Department of Environmental Protection
State Office Building
Hartford, CT 06106
(203) 566-2905

Delaware

Susan LaPorte
Division of Parks and Recreation
Department of Natural Resources and Environmental
    Control
Edward Tatnall Building
P.O. Box 1401
Dover, DE 19901
(302) 736-5284

District of Columbia

William H. Rumsey
Recreation Department
3149 Sixteenth Street, NW
Washington, DC 20010
(202) 629-7313

Florida

David B. Stevenson
Recreation Planner
Bureau of Recreation Planning and Local Assistance
Division of Recreation and Parks
Department of Natural Resources
3900 Commonwealth Boulevard
Tallahassee, FL 32303
(904) 488-4860

Georgia

Harvey G. Young
Department of Natural Resources
Room 815-O
270 Washington Street, NW
Atlanta, GA 30334
(404)656-3530

Hawaii

Susumu Ono
Chairman
Board of Land and Natural Resources
P.O. Box 621
Honolulu, HI 96809
(808) 548-6550

Idaho

Todd Graeff
Chief
Comprehensive Planning Bureau
Department of Parks and Recreation
Statehouse
2177 Warm Springs Avenue
Boise, ID 83720
(208) 334-2154

Illinois

Greg Tichacek
Comprehensive Planning
Division of Planning and Information
Department of Conservation
Lincoln Tower Plaza
524 S. Second Street
Springfield, IL 62706
(217) 782-3884

Indiana

Joseph Payne
Chief
Streams and Trails Section
Division of Outdoor Recreation
Department of Natural Resources
612 State Office Building
Indianapolis, IN 46204
(317) 232-4070

Iowa

Kevin Szcrodronski
Coordinator
Protected Water Areas Study
Iowa State Conservation Commission
Wallace State Office Building
Des Moines, IA 50319
(515) 281-8674

Kansas

Lynn Burris, Jr.
Director
Kansas Park and Resources Authority
503 Kansas Avenue
P.O. Box 977
Topeka, KS 66601
(913) 296-2281

Kentucky

Robert Gunkler
Division of Water
Department of Natural Resources and Environmental
    Protection
18 Reilly Road
Ft. Boone Plaza
Frankfort, KY 40601
(502) 564-3410, ext. 299

Louisiana

Charles Killebrew
Louisiana Natural Rivers System
Department of Wildlife and Fish
P.O. Box 15570
Baton Rouge, LA 70895
(504) 342-5868

Maine

Thomas J. Cieslinski
Environmental Resource Planner
Department of Conservation
State House Station 19
Augusta, ME 04333
(207) 289-3821

Maryland

Isedora Ballerd
Chief
Scenic Rivers Program
Department of Natural Resources
Tawes State Office Building
Annapolis, MD 21401
(301) 269-3656

Massachusetts

Katherine Preston
Scenic Rivers Program
Department of Environmental Management
100 Cambridge Street
Boston, MA 02202
(617) 727-3160

Michigan

Douglas Carter
Department of Natural Resources
P.O. Box 30028
Lansing, MI 48909
(517) 373-3328

Minnesota

Paul T. Swensen
Supervisor
Rivers Section
Department of Natural Resources
444 Lafayette Road
Space Center Building
Box 11
St. Paul, MN 55101
(612) 296-0568

Mississippi

Ken Gordon
Program Coordinator
Mississippi Natural Heritage Program
Mississippi Museum of Natural Science
111 N. Jefferson Street
Jackson, MS 39202
(601) 354-7303

Missouri

Fred Lafser
Director
   or
Rick Pershall
Resource Planner
Department of Natural Resources
P.O. Box 176
Jefferson City, MO 65102
(314) 751-4422

Montana

Ron Holliday
Administrator
Parks Division
Department of Fish, Wildlife and Parks
1420 E. Sixth Avenue
Helena, MT 59620
(406) 449-3750

Nebraska

Verlon K. Vrana
Chief
Planning Division
Natural Resources Commission
P.O. Box 94876
Lincoln, NE 68509
(402) 471-2081

Nevada

Roland Westergard
Director
Department of Conservation and Natural Resources
Capital Complex
201 S. Fall Street
Nye Building, Room 214
Carson City, NV 89701
(702) 885-4360

New Hampshire

David Hartman
Office of State Planning
2½ Beacon Street
Concord, NH 03301
(603) 271-2155

New Jersey

Celeste Tracy
Department of Environmental Protection
109 W. State Street
Trenton, NJ 08625
(609) 292-2455

New Mexico

Karen Brown
SCORP Planner
Natural Resource Department
Villagra Building
Santa Fe, NM 87503
(503) 827-5531

New York

Charles C. Morrison, Jr.
Chief
State Rivers Program
Department of Environmental Conservation
50 Wolf Road, Room 412
Albany, NY 12233
(518) 457-7433

John Banta
Adirondack Park Agency
P.O. Box 99
Ray Brook, NY 12977
(518) 891-4050

North Carolina

Kay Scott
Rivers/Trails Coordinator
Department of Natural Resources and Community
    Development
P.O. Box 27687
Raleigh, NC 27611
(919) 733-7795

North Dakota

Tim Mueller
Assistant Director of Recreation
Parks and Recreation Department
P.O. Box 700
Bismarck, ND 58502
(701) 224-4887

Ohio

Stuart Lewis
Administrator
Scenic Rivers Program
Department of Natural Resources
Fountain Square
Columbus, OH 43224
(614) 265-6460

Oklahoma

John Shannon
Administrator
Oklahoma Scenic Rivers Commission
P.O. Box 292
Tahlequah, OK 74464
(914) 456-3251

Oregon

John E. Lilly
Assistant Administrator
Rivers Program
Parks and Recreation Division
Department of Transportation
525 Trade Street, SE
Salem, OR 97310
(503) 378-5000

Pennsylvania

Roger Fickes
Chief
State and Local Coordinating Section
Division of Outdoor Recreation
Department of Environmental Resources
Third and Riley Streets
Harrisburg, PA 17120
(717) 787-6674

Puerto Rico

Cesar deJesus
Puerto Rico Recreation Development Company
P.O. Box 2923
San Juan, PR 00903

Rhode Island

Judith Benedict
Rivers Coordinator
Division of Planning and Development
Department of Environmental Management
83 Park Street
Providence, RI 02903
(401) 277-2776

South Carolina

Steve Snyder
Scenic Rivers Coordinator
Box 50506
1001 Harden Street, Suite 250
Columbia, SC 29250
(803) 758-2514

South Dakota

Douglas Hofer
Division of Parks and Recreation
Department of Game Fish and Parks
Anderson Building
Pierre, SD 57501
(605) 773-3391

Tennessee

Rick Harwell
Department of Conservation
701 Broadway Avenue
Nashville, TN 37204
(615) 742-6679

Texas

Suzanne Carter
Rivers and Waterways Planning
Parks and Wildlife Department
4200 Smith School Road
Austin, TX 78744
(512) 479-4900

Utah

Chauncey Powlis
Federal/State Coordinator
Department of Natural Resources
1636 W. North Temple
Salt Lake City, UT 84116
(801) 533-5356

Vermont

Stephen Sease
Director
Planning Division
Agency of Environmental Conservation
State Office Building
Montpelier, VT 05602
(802) 828-3357

Virginia

John F. Heerwald
Commission of Outdoor Recreation
James Monroe Building
101 N. 14th Street
Richmond, VA 23219
(804) 225-3014

Washington

Dan Barth
Division of Marine Land Management
River Management
Department of Natural Resources
Olympia, WA 98504
(206) 753-0713

West Virginia

David C. Callaghan
Director
Department of Natural Resources
1800 Washington Street, East
Charleston, WV 23505
(304) 348-2754

Wisconsin

Arthur Doll
Department of Natural Resources
P.O. Box 7921
Madison, WI 53707
(608) 266-0818

Wyoming

Paul Cleary
Natural Resource Analyst
State Planning Coordinator's Office
2320 Capital Avenue
Cheyenne, WY 82002
(307) 777-7574

Jan Wilson
Director
Wyoming Recreation Commission
1920 Thomes Street
Cheyenne, WY 82002
(307) 777-7695

Gary Stevenson
Wyoming Recreation Commission
Trails Coordinator
1920 Thomes Street
Cheyenne, WY 82002
(307) 777-6300

Appendix D: Case-Study Program Managers

For more information on the river conservation projects discussed in this guide, contact:

The Housatonic Valley Association

Ralph H. Goodno, Jr.
Executive Director
Housatonic Valley Association, Inc.
P.O. Box 515
Kent, CT 06757
(203) 927-4649

The Brandywine Conservancy

H. William Sellers
Director
Environmental Management Center
P.O. Box 141
Chadds Ford, PA 19317
(215) 388-7601

The Yakima River Greenway

Richard Anderwald
Planning Director
Yakima County
Room 417, Courthouse
Yakima, WA 98901
(509) 575-4124
Toll-free: (800) 572-7354

Doug Peters
P.O. Box 156
Selah, WA 98942
(509) 697-7201

The Saco River Corridor Commission

Margaret Roy
Executive Director
Saco River Corridor Commission
P.O. Box 283
Main Street
Cornish, ME 04020

The Mississippi Headwaters Board

Lloyd Nesseth
Executive Director
Mississippi Headwaters Board
Cass County Courthouse
Walker, MN 56484
(218) 547-3300, ext. 263

Maine's Comprehensive Approach

Thomas J. Cieslinski
Environmental Resource Planner
Department of Conservation
State House Station 19
Augusta, ME 04333
(207) 289-3821

Massachusetts's Scenic Rivers Program

Katherine Preston
Scenic Rivers Program
Department of Environmental Management
100 Cambridge Street
Boston, MA 02202
(617) 727-3160

Oregon's Riparian Tax Incentive Program

Tony Fast
Riparian Program Coordinator
Riparian Tax Incentive Program
Department of Fish and Wildlife
P.O. Box 3503
Portland, OR 97208
(503) 229-5551

Appendix E: National Wild And Scenic Rivers

Allagash, Maine
Alagnak, Alaska
Alatna, Alaska
Andreafsky, Alaska
Aniakchak, Alaska
Beaver Creek, Alaska
Birch Creek, Alaska
Charley, Alaska
Chattooga, Georgia, South Carolina, and North Carolina
Chilikadrotna, Alaska
Delta, Alaska
Eel, California
Eleven Point, Missouri
Flathead, Montana
Fortymile, Alaska
Gulkana, Alaska
Ivishak, Alaska
John, Alaska
Klamath, California
Kobuk, Alaska
Little Beaver, Ohio
Little Miami, Ohio

Lower American, California
Lower St. Croix, Minnesota and Wisconsin
Middle Delaware, New York, New Jersey, and Pennsylvania
Middle Fork Clearwater, Idaho
Middle Fork Feather, California
Middle Fork Salmon, Idaho
Missouri, Montana, South Dakota, and Nebraska
Mulchatna, Alaska
Noatak, Alaska
North Fork American, California
North Fork Koyukuk, Alaska
Nowitna, Alaska
Obed, Tennessee
Pere Marquette, Michigan
Rapid, Idaho
Rio Grande, Texas and New Mexico
Rogue, Oregon
Salmon, Alaska
Salmon, Idaho
Selawik, Alaska
Sheenjek, Alaska
Skagit, Washington
Smith, California
Snake, Idaho and Oregon
South Fork New River, North Carolina
St. Joe, Idaho
Tinayguk, Alaska
Tlikakila, Alaska
Trinity, California
Unalakleet, Alaska
Upper Delaware, New York and Pennsylvania
Upper St. Croix, Minnesota and Wisconsin
Wind, Alaska
Wolf, Wisconsin

Appendix F: Major Federal Laws Applicable to River Conservation

Of the many federal laws and executive orders that affect rivers directly and indirectly, the following are the most important:

Clean Water Act (33 U.S.C. 1251-1376)—The Federal Water Pollution Control Act Amendments of 1972 (now called the Clean Water Act) was established to restore and maintain the chemical, physical, and biological integrity of the United States's waters. Provides for control of discharges into rivers both from point and nonpoint sources. Administered by the U.S. Environmental Protection Agency (EPA) and state agencies.

Coastal Zone Management Act (16 U.S.C. 1457-64)—Seeks to protect and enhance coastal resources such as wetlands, tidal areas, beaches, and dunes. Is largely a funding program for state coastal-zone management plans, and participation by states is voluntary. Provides that federal action within coastal zones subject to approved state plans must be consistent with those plans. Detailed procedures must be followed when there is a conflict. Administered by the Office of Coastal Zone Management (OCZM) of the National Oceanic and Atmospheric Administration within the U.S. Department of Commerce. OCZM publishes regulations to guide state plans, provides technical assistance, and approves grants.

Department of Transportation Act of 1966, Section 4(f) (49 U.S.C. 1651-59) — Forbids the U.S. Department of Transportation from sponsoring or approving projects that would use or adversely affect either publicly owned land that is important for wildlife and recreation or historic properties, unless there is no "prudent and feasible alternative."

Endangered Species Act (16 U.S.C. 1531-43) — Requires all federal agencies to take whatever action is necessary to ensure that their activities do not jeopardize endangered species or habitat critical to their survival. Administered by the Fish and Wildlife Service within the U.S. Department of the Interior.

Federal Power Act (16 U.S.C. 791 *et seq.*) — Requires that every hydroelectric project that is on federal land or a navigable stream or that would feed into interstate power grids be approved by the Federal Energy Regulatory Commission (FERC). Citizens have a right to participate in this process and raise environmental issues that FERC must consider.

Other important energy and utility laws that affect river conservation are:

- *Crude Oil Windfall Profit Tax Act of 1980*, P.L. 96-223, 94 Stat. 229 *et seq.* (miscellaneous U.S. Code cites).
- *Energy Security Act*, P.L. 96-294, 94 Stat. 611 (miscellaneous U.S. Code cites).
- *Public Utility Regulatory Policies Act of 1978*, P.L. 95-617, 92 Stat. 3117 (miscellaneous U.S. Code cites).

Fish and Wildlife Coordination Act (16 U.S.C. 661-661c) — Provides that wildlife conservation shall receive equal consideration with other factors in water-resource-development projects. Requires that whenever a river is altered or impounded by any federal agency or pursuant to a federal permit, then the responsible agency must consult with the U.S. Fish and Wildlife Service and similar state agencies and consider steps to conserve wildlife resources.

Floodplain Management Executive Order 11988 and the National Flood Insurance Program (42 U.S.C. 4001-4128) —Taken together, the executive order and National Flood Insurance Program (NFIP) direct federal agencies to take action to reduce the risk of flood loss, minimize the impact of floods on human safety, and restore and preserve the natural and beneficial values served by floodplains. Special evaluation and notification requirements are placed on federal actions (projects, funding, permits, etc.) that will result in floodplain development. The NFIP provides insurance for building in designated floodplains only if the applicable local government has an approved plan that restricts development in flood-prone lands.

National Environmental Policy Act (42 U.S.C. 4321-47) — Requires all federal agencies to consider the impact of their actions on the human environment. Actions can be direct (dam building) or indirect (federal funding or permits). Requires filing of an environmental-impact statement (EIS) for major federal actions significantly affecting the environment. Administered by the President's Council on Environmental Quality and the U.S. EPA.

The Rivers and Harbors Act of 1899 (33 U.S.C. 401-13) — Makes it unlawful to construct any structure (dams, bridges, piers, etc.) in any navigable water or to deposit refuse therein without federal approval. In combination with Section 404 of the Clean Water Act and federal regulations, this law establishes a permit system for building, dredging, and filling in navigable waterways. Special emphasis is to be placed on water quality and other environmental values in issuing any permits for such activities. Administered by the U.S. Army Corps of Engineers, which must consult with the U.S. EPA and other agencies before giving approval.

Soil Conservation Act (16 U.S.C. 590a *et seq.*) — Directs the U.S. Soil Conservation Service (SCS) to prevent soil erosion, control floods, maintain river navigability and protect public health. The goals are carried out in a variety of ways, including collecting data, funding erosion-control projects, and providing technical assistance. The SCS, an agency within the U.S. Department of Agriculture, works primarily with local soil conservation districts and farmers. The local districts generally have authority to impose land-use and soil-erosion control regulations and initiate watershed improvement projects.

Surface Mining and Reclamation Act (30 U.S.C. 1201 *et seq.*) — Establishes nationwide environmental control over strip mining. Prohibits certain strip-mining practices and requires reclamation of land after mining. Prime farmlands are provided special protection as are water supplies. Administered by the Office of Surface Mining within the U.S. Department of the Interior.

Wetlands Protection Executive Order 11990 — Stresses the importance of protecting wetlands and directs federal agencies to take action to minimize harm to and preserve and enhance values of wetlands. Agencies are also directed to avoid undertaking construction or projects that damage wetlands unless there is no practicable alternative.

Wild and Scenic Rivers Act (16 U.S.C. 1271-87) — Establishes a policy designating that rivers that possess certain outstanding features and values shall be preserved in a free-flowing condition. Also provides for technical assistance to local governments and citizen groups. Administered by the National Park Service within the U.S. Department of the Interior.

Appendix G: Measuring the Values of River Conservation

Efforts to conserve rivers are sometimes countered by arguments that the water is too valuable to allow it to run free. Certainly, the economic benefits that water provides when used by industries, for irrigation, or to generate electricity are obvious. But water can also provide economic benefits when left in its natural state, though these may be less obvious and are more difficult to quantify.

Many of the benefits of river conservation accrue to people using a waterway for recreational and other purposes. But people who do not use the river may also value its conservation. Some may value having an option to use the river sometime in the future even though they do not intend to do so in the present ("option value"). Some may place a value on allowing future generations to inherit undeveloped rivers so that they can make their own decisions how they should be used ("bequest value"). And someone living far from a river who never intends to visit it may nevertheless care strongly about conserving the waterway in its natural state ("existence value").

The importance of both the user and nonuser benefits of river

This appendix was written by Edwin H. Clark II, Jennifer A. Haverkamp, and Phillip C. Metzger.

conservation is growing rapidly because of the increased interest in outdoor recreation and in environmental amenities in general. Table G.1, for example, summarizes the most recent information available on participation rates in outdoor recreation activities. Table G.2 projects the growth in demand for various water-related activities through the year 2000. Many recreational activities that require instream flow, such as canoeing and fishing, are expected to grow substantially faster than either national population or personal income.[1]

Table G.1

Participation in Water-Related Recreation Activities, by Federal-Land Visitor Survey Respondents, 1976-77

Water-dependent activities	Percentage participating
Fishing	59
Swimming or sunbathing, not in pools	50
Water skiiing	22
Canoe, kayak, river running	16
Sailing	10
Other boating	33
Ice skating	9
Activities possibly enhanced by flowing water	
Picnicking	61
Camping (developed area)	57
Nature walks, birdwatching, wildlife photography*	44
Hiking or backpacking*	35
Camping (primitive area)	26
Hunting*	19
Horseback riding*	12

* Participation rate is based on activity involvement anywhere, not just on the federal land where the survey was performed.

Source: *3rd National Outdoor Recreation Plan, Appendix I* (Washington, D.C.: U.S. Department of the Interior, 1979), p. 2.

Only a few attempts to estimate the economic value of such activities have been made, and those efforts do not provide an adequate basis for determining the overall economic value of protecting any particular river. Studies that could provide estimates and include all the values would be difficult and usually expensive. For instance, it is hard to estimate a river's values to nonusers; there is no accepted method for estimating the value of nongame wildlife in and along a river. Nevertheless, the studies that have been done do indicate that the values of preservation can be very

Table G.2

Projected Growth in Demand for Water-Related Activities through the Year 2000

Water-dependent Activities	1977	1990	2000
Fishing (freshwater)	100	118	139
Swimming (outdoor)	100	114	127
Water skiing	100	109	117
Canoeing	100	121	140
Sailing	100	144	182
Other boating	100	119	136
Ice skating	100	123	143
Activities possibly enhanced by flowing water			
Picnicking	100	112	124
Camping (developed area)	100	116	150
Nature study	100	110	110
Hiking	100	109	117
Camping (dispersed)	100	116	133
Hunting (waterfowl)	100	119	113
Hunting (small game)	100	106	109
Horseback riding	100	109	118

Source: U.S. Department of Agriculture, *Soil and Water Resources Act 1980 Appraisal, Part II: Soil, Water, and Related Resources in the United States—Analysis of Resource Trends* (Washington, D.C.: U.S. Department of Agriculture, August 1981), p. 193.

significant. Most of these studies have focused on recreational values associated with fishing, although there have been some efforts to look at white-water rafting and other recreational uses. Probably the most comprehensive recent effort to determine the value of sports fishing was published by Resources for the Future.[2] In a poll of operators of fishing areas throughout the United States, information was gathered about the costs that anglers voluntarily incur and the distances they travel. This study estimated that a day of fishing was worth between $7 and $24, depending in part on the type of fish available at the site (see table G.3).

Table G.3

Estimates of Recreational Fishing Value

Type of Angling	Value Per Day	
	Low	High
Cold-water game fish	$10.96	$24.09
Warm-water game fish/panfish	9.65	21.43
Catfish/rough fish	7.00	16.03

Source: William J. Vaughan and Clifford S. Russell, *Freshwater Recreational Fishing* (Washington, D.C.: Resources for the Future, 1982), p. 148.

A study published in 1974 estimated that the value of a salmon fishery in the Fraser River, British Columbia, amounted to $183 per year per household in the Upper River and $436 for the Lower River.[3] A 1981 study of Summit Creek, Utah, estimated that each "angler day" was worth $43.59.[4]

A study of recreational benefits in the Poudre River, Colorado, published in 1979, attempted to establish the comparative worth of different types of activities and how they were affected by the amount of river flow.[5] This study found that individuals using the river for white-water rafting and canoeing were willing to pay two to ten times as much (up to $5 per person per day of use) as anglers and people picnicking or walking along the shore. However, because the latter activities had many more people engaged in them, their total value was higher. This study concluded that, during some seasons, economic benefits might be increased if more water were left in the river rather than diverted for irrigation. The study also pointed out that recreational use of the river was increasing faster than was the value of alternative uses of the water. At the current growth rate, recreational values would approximately double over a 10-year period, raising the question of whether it would be efficient to make essentially irreversible changes to the river (such as building a new reservoir) that would prevent these values from being realized.

The strength of demand for scenic rivers with good white water is reflected in the rapid growth in commercial white-water rafting trips throughout the country. On the Colorado River, to take an extreme case, the number of raft trips through the Grand Canyon increased from 372 in 1962 to 16,432 in 1972 — over 4,000 percent. Prior to 1949, less than 100 people had ever made this run. On many rivers, authorities have had to ration the number of rafts on the river to avoid overcrowding, which could reduce a rafter's enjoyment, create dangerous conditions, and seriously affect the quality of the riparian environment. On the Colorado River, the National Park Service now has limited the number of people going through the Grand Canyon to 14,000 per year.

Recreational activities can also contribute to an area's economy. For instance, in Utah, resident anglers spent an average of $12.30 per day fishing cold-water streams in 1975; nonresidents spent $34.30 each.[6] In its 1980 survey, the U.S. Fish and Wildlife Service found that hunters spent an average of $490 per year ($26 per day spent fishing) and freshwater anglers an average of $214 per year ($11 per day spent fishing).[7]

But the values of rivers extend far beyond the recreational benefits they provide to people who hunt along them, boat on them, or fish and swim in them. They provide valuable habitat for species other than game birds and fish. Over half the U.S. adult population enjoys some form of wildlife observation, photography, feeding, or other nonconsumptive activity.[8] Wetlands along a river's banks remove contaminants from water, control floods, and moderate water supplies.[9] Although there is substantial debate about how to place monetary values on these benefits, there is little question about their importance.

One recent attempt to estimate nonuser benefits of river conservation related to the quality (not the quantity) of water in Colorado's Platte River.[10] This study used surveys to estimate the value that people in the area were willing to pay "for the knowledge that the natural environment exists as a habitat for fish, wildlife, and other ecosystems" even though those people did not directly use that environment or the wildlife. Nonusers living in the Denver and Fort Collins metropolitan areas indicated that these two elements of the conservation value were worth an average of $59 annually. In addition, residents were willing to pay an average of $26 a year for the option to make use of the Platte, an amount equivalent to 40 percent of what they were willing to pay for their improved recreational opportunities. In short, this study found that the combined worth of option value, bequest value, and existence value exceeded the actual recreational value of the water.

References

1. U.S. Department of Agriculture, *Soil and Water Resources Conservation Act 1980 Appraisal, Part II: Soil, Water, and Related Resources in the United States — Analysis of Resource Trends* (Washington, D.C.: U.S. Department of Agriculture, August 1981), p. 193.

2. William J. Vaughan and Clifford S. Russell, *Freshwater Recreational Fishing* (Washington, D.C.: Resources for the Future, 1982), pp. 147-48.

3. Philip A. Meyer, *Recreational and Preservation Values Associated with the Salmon of the Fraser River*, Information Report Series no. PAC/N-74-1 (Vancouver, B.C.: Environment Canada Fisheries and Marine Service, 1974), pp. 15-17.

4. William H. Geer, "Assessment of Trout Fishery Conditions in Summit Creek (Utah County) under Two Scenarios of Hydroelectric Generating Station Operation," Utah Division of Wildlife Resources Technical Report, September 1981, p. 8.

5. John T. Daubert and Robert A. Young (with S. Lee Gray), *Economic*

Benefits from Instream Flow in a Colorado Mountain Stream, Completion Report no. 91 (Fort Collins, Colo.: Colorado Water Resources Research Institute, Colorado State University, June 1979).

6. M. Allred, *Public Opinion Survey of Fishing and Hunting Activities in Utah*, Publication no. 76-23 (Salt Lake City, Utah: Utah Division of Wildlife Resources, 1976).

7. U.S. Department of the Interior, Fish and Wildlife Service, and U.S. Department of Commerce, Bureau of the Census, *1980 National Survey of Fishing, Hunting, and Wildlife-Associated Recreation* (Washington, D.C.: U.S. Government Printing Office, 1982), pp. 11, 21.

8. Ibid., pp. 30-34.

9. Brandt Richardson, ed., *Selected Proceedings of the Midwest Conference on Wetlands Values and Management: June 17-19, 1981* (Navarre, Minn.: The Freshwater Society, 1981).

10. Douglas A. Greenley, Richard G. Walsh, and Robert A. Young, *Economic Benefits of Improved Water Qaulity: Public Perceptions of Option and Preservation Values* (Boulder, Colo.: Westview Press, 1982).

Bibliography

General Studies

Amos, William H. *The Infinite River*. New York: Ballantine Books. 1972.

Amos, William H. *Limnology: An Introduction to the Freshwater Environment*. Chestertown, Md.: LaMotte Chemical Products Company. 1969.

Brown, A. L. *Ecology of Fresh Water*. Cambridge, Mass.: Harvard University Press. 1971.

Dearinger, John A., and Woolwine, George. *Measuring the Intangible Values of Natural Streams*. Lexington, Ky.: University of Kentucky. Kentucky Water Resources Research Institute. Part I — 1971. Part II — 1973.

Kauffmann, John M. *Flow East: A Look at Our North Atlantic Rivers*. New York: McGraw-Hill Book Company. 1973.

Leopold, A. *A Sand County Almanac*. New York: Sierra Club/Ballantine Books. 1970.

Leopold, Luna B. *Quantitative Comparisons of Some Aesthetic Factors Among Rivers*. Circular no. 620. Washington, D.C.: U.S. Geological Survey. 1969.

Litton, Burton, and Tetlow, Robert. *Water and the Landscape*. Port Washington, N.Y.: Water Information Center, Inc. 1974.

Seymour, P. *The Living River: The Romance, History and Beauty of Our Nation's Waterways*. Kansas City, Mo.: Hallmark Crown Editions. 1973.

Teal, J. *Life and Death of the Salt Marsh*. New York: Audubon/Ballantine Books. 1969.

Unsinger, R. L. *The Life of Rivers and Streams*. New York: McGraw-Hill Book Company. 1967.

Ward, R.C. *Principles of Hydrology*. New York: McGraw-Hill Book Company. 1975.

Case Studies

Atlanta Regional Commission. *Chattahoochee Corridor Study*. Atlanta, Ga.: Atlanta Regional Commission. 1972.

Bennington County (Vt.) Regional Commission. *The Vermont River: Heritage and Promise*. Arlington, Vt.: Bennington County Regional Commission. 1975.

Cultural Benefits from Metropolitan River Recreation San Antonio Prototype. College Station, Tex.: Texas A & M University. 1972.

An Inventory and Evaluation of the Environmental Aesthetic and Recreational Resources of the Upper Sustina River, Alaska. Seattle, Wash.: Jones and Jones. 1975.

Maine Department of Conservation. *Allagash Wilderness Waterway: Visitor Use and Visitor Characteristics.* Augusta, Me.: Maine Department of Conservation. 1974.

Maryland Department of Natural Resources. *Deer Creek: Scenic River, A Guide to the Protection and Wise Use of Deer Creek.* Annapolis, Md.: Maryland Department of Natural Resources. 1978.

The Nature Conservancy. And U.S. Department of the Interior. Bureau of Outdoor Recreation. Mid-Continent Regional Office. *The Blackfoot River: A Conservation and Recreation Management Plan.* Portland, Oreg.: Nature Conservancy. 1976.

The Nooksack Plan: A Documented Approach to the Inventory and Evaluation of a River System. Seattle, Wash. Jones and Jones. 1973.

New Jersey Department of Environmental Protection. Delaware & Raritan Canal Commission. *Delaware & Raritan Canal State Park: Vegetation and Aquatic Buffer Zone Study.* Trenton, N.J.: New Jersey Department of Environmental Protection. 1977.

U.S. Department of the Interior. Bureau of Outdoor Recreation. Northeast Region. *New River Gorge.* Philadelphia, Pa.: Bureau of Outdoor Recreation. 1975.

U.S. Department of the Interior. Bureau of Outdoor Recreation. South Central Regional Office. *Lower Rio Grande: A Case Study.* Albuquerque, N.M.: New Mexico State Planning Office. 1975.

Wharton, Charles. *Southern River Swamp: A Multiple-Use Environment.* Atlanta, Ga.: Georgia State University. 1970.

Zube, Ervin H.; Pitts, David; and Anderson, Thomas. *Perception and Measurement of Scenic Resources in the Southern Connecticut River Valley.* Amherst, Mass.: Institute for Man and His Environment. 1974.

Getting Started

Eugster, J. Glenn. "A Landsaver's Journal: Adventures in the Garden of the Great Spirit." *American Land Forum Magazine.* Spring 1983.

Migel, J. Michael, editor. *The Stream Conservation Handbook: The First Practical Primer for Fishermen.* New York: Crown Publishers, 1974.

National Trust for Historic Preservation. *Preserving Large Estates.* Information sheet no. 34. Washington, D.C.: National Trust for Historic Preservation. 1982.

Natural Lands Trust, Inc. *The Use and Protection of Privately Held Natural Lands.* Philadelphia, Pa.: The Natural Lands Trust, Inc. 1982.

U.S. Department of the Interior. Office of the Assistant Secretary for Fish and Wildlife in Parks. *New Tools for Land Protection: An Introductory Handbook.* Washington, D.C.: U.S. Government Printing Office. 1982.

Understanding the Issues

Chubb, Michael, and Bauman, Eric. *The RIVERS Method: A Pilot Study of River Recreation Potential Assessment.* East Lansing, Mich.: Michigan State University. Department of Geography. 1976.

Maine Office of Energy Resources. *Maine Comprehensive Hydropower Plan.* Augusta, Me.: Maine Office of Energy Resources. 1983.

Natural Resources Council of Maine. *Environmentally Acceptable Hydropower in Maine.* Augusta, Me.: The Natural Resources Council of Maine. 1983.

New England River Basin Commission. *Water, Watts, and Wilds: Hydropower and Competing Uses in New England.* The Final Report of the commission. Boston: New England River Basin Commission. 1981.

Virginia Commission of Outdoor Recreation. *Virginia's Scenic Rivers*. Richmond, Va.: Virginia Commission of Outdoor Recreation. 1969.

Using Basic Conservation Tools

Iowa Natural Heritage Foundation. *The Landowner's Options: A Guide to the Voluntary Protection of Land in Iowa*. Des Moines, Iowa: Iowa Natural Heritage Foundation. 1982.

Maine Coast Heritage Trust. *The Landowner's Options: A Guide to the Voluntary Protection of Land in Maine*. Northeast Harbor, Me.: Maine Coast Heritage Trust. 1978.

Montana Land Reliance. *Conservation Law Seminar: Conservation Easements and Related Charitable Conveyances*. Helena, Montana Land Reliance. 1982.

Ottauquechee Regional Land Trust, The Nature Conservancy, Lake Camplain Islands Trust, and Vermont Natural Resources Council. *Charitable Gifts of Land: A Landowner's Guide to Vermont and Federal Tax Incentives*. 1982.

University of Delaware. Water Resources Center. *Water Resources Protection Measures in Land Development: A Handbook*. Newark, N.J.: University of Delaware. 1974.

Choosing a Strategy

Atlanta Regional Commission. *Review Manual Technical Appendix III: Procedures for Review of Certificates under the Metropolitan River Protection Act*. Atlanta, Ga.: Atlanta Regional Commission. 1977.

Maine Department of Conservation. *The Maine Rivers Study*. Augusta, Me.: Maine Department of Conservation. 1983.

Maine State Park and Recreation Commission. *Saco River Corridor: Open Space and Recreation Potential.* Augusta, Me.: Maine State Park and Recreation Commission. 1969.

National Parks and Conservation Association. *Greenline Parks: Land Conservation Trends for the Eighties and Beyond.* Washington, D.C.: National Parks and Conservation Association. 1983.

Pennsylvania Department of Environmental Resources. *Pennsylvania Scenic River System: Citizen Participation Guidelines.* Harrisburg, Pa.: Pennsylvania Department of Environmental Resources. 1975.

Pennsylvania Department of Environmental Resources. *Pennsylvania Scenic Rivers Inventory.* Harrisburg, Pa.: Pennsylvania Department of Environmental Resources. 1975.

Philadelphia City Planning Commission. *Wissahickon Watershed Development Guide.* Philadelphia, Pa.: Philadelphia City Planning Commission. 1976.

U.S. Department of the Interior. Bureau of Outdoor Recreation. Northeast Region. *A Look at the Wild and Scenic Rivers Act.* Philadelphia, Pa.: Bureau of Outdoor Recreation. 1974.

U.S. Department of the Interior. Heritage Conservation and Recreation Service. Northeast Region. *Viewpoints on the Impacts of National Wild and Scenic River Designation.* Philadelphia, Pa.: Heritage Conservation and Recreation Service. 1978.

U.S. Department of the Interior. National Park Service. *Conserving the Garden of the Great Spirit: St. Lawrence River-Thousand Island Area Report.* Philadelphia, Pa.: National Park Service. 1983.

U.S. Department of the Interior. National Park Service. *Farmington River Study.* Philadelphia, Pa.: National Park Service. 1984.

U.S. Department of the Interior. National Park Service. *Greenway Planning: A Conservation Strategy for Significant Landscapes.* Philadelphia, Pa.: National Park Service. 1983.

U.S. Department of the Interior. National Park Service. *A Greenway Strategy for Weems Creek.* Philadelphia, Pa.: National Park Service. 1982.

U. S. Department of the Interior. National Park Service. *The Housatonic in Connecticut: A Wild and Scenic River Study.* Washington, D.C.: National Park Service. 1979.

U.S. Department of the Interior. National Park Service. *How to Work with the System.* Philadelphia, Pa.: National Park Service. 1979.

U.S. Department of the Interior. National Park Service. *Maine Rivers Study.* Philadelphia, Pa.: National Park Service. 1982.

U.S. Department of the Interior. National Park Service. *Maryland Rivers Study.* Philadelphia, Pa.: National Park Service, 1983.

U.S. Department of the Interior. National Park Service. *Nationwide Rivers Inventory.* Washington, D.C.: National Park Service. 1982.

U.S. Department of the Interior. National Park Service. *Penobscot Wild and Scenic River Study.* Washington, D.C.: National Park Service. 1976.

U.S. Department of the Interior. National Park Service. *The Pine Creek Wild and Scenic River Study.* Washington, D.C.: National Park Service. 1979.

U.S. Department of the Interior. National Park Service. "St. Croix National Scenic Riverway, Minnesota-Wisconsin: Proposed Zoning Standards." *Federal Register* 38, no. 113 (June 13, 1973).

U.S. Department of the Interior. National Park Service. "Section 5(d) Rivers." *Federal Register* 35, no. 210 (October 28, 1970).

U.S. Department of the Interior. National Park Service. *The Shepaug in Connecticut: A Wild and Scenic River Study*. Washington, D.C.: National Park Service. 1979.

U.S. Department of the Interior. National Park Service. *Some Things You Should Know about National Wild and Scenic River Designations*. Philadelphia, Pa.: National Park Service. 1979.

U.S. Department of the Interior. National Park Service. *The Upper Delaware: A Wild and Scenic River Study*. Washington, D.C.: National Park Service. 1976.

U.S. Department of the Interior. National Park Service. *Viewpoints on the Impacts of National Wild and Scenic River Designations*. Philadelphia, Pa.: National Park Service. 1978.

U.S. Department of the Interior. National Park Service. *The Youghiogheny National Wild and Scenic River Study*. Washington, D.C.: National Park Service. 1978.

U.S. Department of the Interior. Tennessee Valley Authority. *Alternatives for Completing the Tellico Project*. Washington, D.C.: Tennessee Valley Authority. 1978.

U.S. Environmental Protection Agency. *The Public Benefits of Cleaned Water: Emerging Greenway Opportunities*. Washington, D.C.: Environmental Protection Agency. 1977.

U.S. General Accounting Office. *Federal Protection and Preservation of Wild and Scenic Rivers Is Slow and Costly*. Washington, D.C.: General Accounting Office. 1978.

The Yakima River Regional Greenway. Seattle, Wash.: Jones and Jones. 1976.

Miscellaneous

Fenneman, Nevin. *Physiography of Eastern United States.* New York: McGraw-Hill Book Company. 1938.

Lull, H. W., and Reinhart, K. G. *Forests and Floods in the Eastern United States.* Research Paper NE-226. Washington, D.C.: U.S. Forest Service. 1972.

Pennsylvania Department of Environmental Resources. And U.S. Department of the Interior. Bureau of Outdoor Recreation. *Summary of Proceedings: Northeast Regional States, Scenic Rivers Planning Workshop.* Philadelphia, Pa.: Bureau of Outdoor Recreation. 1976.

U.S. Department of Agriculture. Forest Service. North Central Forest Experiment Station. *Proceedings: River Management and Research Symposium.* St. Paul, Minn.: U.S. Forest Service. 1977.